Don't miss Barry J. Farber's previous book

DIAMOND IN THE ROUGH

"A tour de force on how to think . . . A MUST-READING for every grade school, high school, and college student. There ought to be courses based on this book in every institution of learning in the country. Then students would learn the things in life that are really important. Your book is a road map!"
—RICHARD J. WALLER,
   Vice-President, TeleRep

"This is destined to be a classic on personal success, however you define it. This book is full of powerful, practical, and remarkably simple ideas that anyone can use immediately to improve any part of their life. I read it in one sitting."
—BRIAN TRACY,
   Brian Tracy International

"Barry J. Farber's book *Diamond in the Rough* is a welcome change! Barry gives practical commonsense ideas about achieving success. In fact, I strongly believe every high school kid should read Barry's book before they graduate or enter the workforce!"
—RICH R. RAGNANESE,
   WERE Talk Radio

"Successful people travel different roads to achieve success. This book illustrates those differences. It was not written about a single road or a single author's opinion. It is about a multitude of roads to success. And the question 'How did they do it?' is answered a hundred different ways.

   "Barry Farber has achieved his own success with this publication. It is far beyond what we would call a 'diamond in the rough.' It's a polished gem."
—DEBRA J. SIECKMAN,
   Director, Sales Development, Allied Van Lines

"Great reading! Anyone who has a desire to achieve something in this world should read this book . . . quick-reading and enjoyable."
—CHANDRAM RAJARATNAM,
   President, SoftChoice Corporation

"Farber has masterfully woven the success factors of top-producing people into chapter after chapter after chapter of his new book."
—PHILIP W. DEZAN,
   Vice-President, Training and Education, Weichert Realtors

"This book gives its readers a pathway for life's journey, proving that there is a true leader within each of us. Whatever your occupation is, you can do better. Barry Farber has convinced me that everybody is a 'diamond in the rough.'"
—RICHARD J. LUISI,
Southeast Area Vice-President, Electrolux Corporation

"Seldom, if ever, has an author been able to reveal the keys to success in a manner that is so easily understood . . . Every person who is concerned with achieving success in their business, or even their own personal lives, should read every page of this book."
—THOMAS B. WILLIAMS,
   Vice-President, National Sales Manager, F. Schumacher and Co.

"Barry Farber provides unique and useful tools for success. His book accurately describes that success is not often a smooth, problem-free ascent to the top of the success ladder; but rather most real success comes at the end of a difficult journey where the obstacles and problems themselves ensure that greater success was achieved."
—JIM IVY, PRESIDENT and CEO,
   Savin Corporation

What people are saying about Barry Farber . . .

"Barry's powerful and practical ideas come from his achievements in the real world of sales and business success. He's made a huge contribution to our national sales force!"
—JOE BOURDOW,
   President, Val-Pak

"Barry Farber's program is the best mental training you can get!"
—BRUCE JENNER,
   Olympic Gold Medalist

"We all very much enjoyed your presentation and certainly your humor, as demonstrated by the standing ovation. Many expressed to me personally how much they enjoyed your stories, thoughts, and perspective of FOCUS."
—BILL GOLLIHER,
   Anderson News Company

"The highest-rated speaker at our conference."
—*Inc.* magazine

"The standing ovation you received was indicative of the revitalized attitude and work efforts that have been displayed since our Kickoff Meeting. This is a direct result of your excellent planning and presentation."
—JEFFREY L. JOHNSON,
   Executive Vice-President, Northern Business Systems

"No esoteric formulas, just plain, straightforward solutions for improved sales."
—STEVE POTTS,
   Minolta

"On target, entertaining and educational. Your concepts are right on."
—MARK VAN HARTESVELT,
   Double Tree Hotels

Berkley Books by Barry J. Farber

DIAMOND IN THE ROUGH
DIAMONDS UNDER PRESSURE

DIAMONDS
under
PRESSURE

*Five Steps to Turning Adversity
Into Success*

BARRY J. FARBER

BERKLEY BOOKS, NEW YORK

This book is an original publication of
The Berkley Publishing Group.

DIAMONDS UNDER PRESSURE

A Berkley Book / published by arrangement with
the author

PRINTING HISTORY
Berkley trade paperback edition / September 1998
Berkley Special Sales edition / January 1999

The Penguin Putnam Inc. World Wide Web site address is
http://www.penguinputnam.com

ISBN: 0-425-17181-7

Special thanks:

To my family . . . for their constant love and support, and for being the greatest way I know to relieve the pressure;

Thanks to all the people who have given their time, and shared their lessons so others could grow;

To Sharyn Kolberg, for the long hours of transcribing and for another flawless performance under pressure;

To Hillary Cige, for going beyond the editing process and adding value to the entire project;

Liz Perl, Barbara O'Shea, Jennifer Schwabinger, and Grace Paik for their extra efforts.

Contents

DIAMONDS
under
PRESSURE

Diamonds under Pressure

IMAGINE YOURSELF BURIED a hundred miles beneath the earth's surface. You are made of carbon crystals, and the weight of the earth pressing in on you from all sides is condensing you into the purest and toughest substance made by nature.

This is but the beginning of your incredible journey. Lying beneath the earth's surface, hidden under tons of crushing earth, volcanic activity begins to squeeze the liquid kimberlite in which you reside. The pressure begins to build, and continues unrelentingly, until the heavy liquid, laden with its precious cargo, can do nothing but explode up to the surface. You, and thousands of other stones like you, are spewed all over the land; others fall back into the volcanic pipe where they are eventually mined.

You are a diamond, and the incredible pressure you have just experienced makes you one of only a very few substances to reach the earth's surface from its remote depths.

Human beings are like diamonds in many ways. Our character, the purest and toughest part of ourselves, is formed deep within us, and often rises to the surface only when the pressure is greatest. When adversity strikes, it can tear us apart, or it can build us up so that we can face whatever else life may bring. What doesn't kill us, makes us stronger.

GALAXIES WITHIN GALAXIES

Once I took my children to the Museum of Natural History, where we watched a film about perspective and the nature of the universe. The narrator drew a small circle in a town square in Italy. We were then shown an aerial photograph of a circle ten times that size, including the entire town. Then another circle ten times that which showed the country, then the continent, then the earth, the planets, the stars, and galaxies within galaxies. Then the process was reversed, until finally we were looking at the tiny microscopic worlds found within a drop of water.

This film had a profound impact on me. I began to think about the universe, about the incredible energy that surrounds us, from the galaxies above to the smallest particles beneath our feet. The world was formed from energies colliding. The universe is exploding and expanding. All that is and ever was, was born from adversity. It is the way of life, the way of nature.

Observing nature tells us that all life evolves through survival of the fittest. Those who are best at withstanding adversity survive to pass their genes on to the next generation. Animals survive adversity, and learn from it, instinctively. Take the caterpillar. The caterpillar builds its cocoon and slowly evolves into a butterfly. If you open a cocoon to try and "help" the butterfly emerge, it will die. Because in order to escape its cocoon, the butterfly must bang its wings against the sides again and again, which gives its wings the strength to fly. Without that obstacle to fight against, the butterfly's wings are too weak to hold it up.

Many animals have evolved compensating factors for deficiencies they have in certain areas. Near blindness, for example, would seem to be a life-threatening impediment for most animals. Take bats, for instance. They can barely see anything at all, yet they fly easily through the darkness. They have developed such a keen sense of hearing that they steer by echo. According to *The Trials of Life* by David Attenborough, they "emit a sound, and then assess the difference in intensity of the sound in each ear and the infinitesimal difference in time that it takes to reach one ear before the other." Hyenas have another way of traveling in the dark. They use their heightened sense of smell. Their nasal membranes are fifty times the size of ours. Attenborough says that "the information they can gather is so great and varied that it is difficult for us to appreciate it. With a sniff, a hyena can perceive not only the here and now, but simultaneously a whole series of events stretching back into the past."

Humans, too, have ways of instinctually adapting to adversity.

Take the story of Marsha Curtis, a talented violinist who suffers from epilepsy. When drug remedies did not work, doctors performed surgery to remove the portion of her brain that was causing her seizures. The first operation was only partially successful, so they did another, and then a third. They were reluctant to perform these operations because they would be cutting right next to the part of the brain that usually controls musical ability and memory. However, they cut three different times, and each time her musical ability remained. The doctors soon realized that since her brain had been damaged by the epilepsy since she was a little girl, a different portion of the brain had already taken over her musical abilities.

These are coping mechanisms that have evolved over hundreds and hundreds of years. The difference between human beings and animals is that we don't have to wait hundreds of years or rely on instinct to find ways of coping with adversity. When adversity strikes, we can make the necessary changes according to the way we perceive and interpret our environment.

Several years back there was a movie produced and directed by Robert Redford called *The Milagro Bean Field War*. The film opened with a wide-angle view of a barren desert landscape. The earth was cracked, brown, and windswept. It was early in the morning, and the sun was already drying out whatever moisture that had been there the night before. As the camera panned in closer, a tumbledown shack came into view. Inside was an old man asleep in a hard, narrow cot. He slowly awoke and painfully arose from the bed. He shuffled over to a mirror on the wall, staring at his wrinkled, worry-worn face. Yet his first words were "Thank you, God, for allowing me to wake and see another day."

There could not be a man in more desolate circumstances. Yet he was thankful to be alive and to see another day. It was his perception that his life was worth living, and that was probably what kept him alive.

There was a study done recently of approximately forty thousand people in the world who are now over one hundred years old. What they had most in common was not their special diet or their exercise routines. The trait they all shared was that they continued to be engaged in life. They interacted with other people, they worked in their gardens, they took an interest in the world around them. They were silly. They laughed and they cried often. Instead of bemoaning the fact that they only had a short time left, they enjoyed every precious moment.

This is a philosophy I heard over and over again when I was writing my last book, *Diamond in the Rough*. That book is about discovering and mining the potential within each of us, and learning to use that potential to achieve success. For the book, I interviewed hundreds of people, from all walks of life, who had achieved extraordinary success.

As I interviewed these people, as I heard their stories of outstanding achievement in business, sports, education, entertainment, science, medicine, and politics, I began to see that they all had something in common. At some point in their lives, they had all fallen short of their goals. That is to say, not one of these people had traveled a smooth, unobstructed road to success. They had run into adversity, challenges, setbacks, conflicts, stress, rejection, disappointment, defeat, and frustration. They had all stumbled and fallen. Just like the rest of us.

But what made these people stand out above the rest was what they did when things went wrong.

Abraham Lincoln lost eight elections, had two failed businesses, went into bankruptcy, and suffered a nervous breakdown that kept him in bed for six months. However, after losing a bid for the senate, he said, "The path was worn and slippery. My foot slipped from under me, knocking the other out of the way, but I recovered and said to myself, 'It's a slip and not a fall.' "

Henry Ford failed in business and went broke five times before he encountered success. Yet he once said, "One who fears, limits his activities. Failure is only the opportunity to more intelligently begin again."

The only way to get to success is to understand failure. *Every* successful person has had to face his or her share of adversity, obstacles, and outright defeat. *Every* successful person has had to struggle with deep-seated fears and self-doubt. And every successful person has learned how to put fear and failure into proper perspective, to gain strength and knowledge from difficulty. They *use* their mistakes—in fact, they benefit from them. What makes these ordinary people extraordinary is that they face mistakes and adversity head-on and come out the other side better for the experience. They know that success only comes from repeated triumph over adverse conditions, and that mistakes provide information for future attempts.

There's a very fine line between achieving our dreams and fulfilling our potential, and building a life based on timidity and compromise. This book provides a *realistic, practical antidote* to the immobilizing fear of failure. If you look at mistakes, disappointments, barriers, and failures as building blocks toward future success, you can move past the hardships and try again. Every failure provides a lesson, and every lesson learned prepares us for a new attempt.

Olympic great Bruce Jenner knows all about fear, and the fear of failure. As a child, Jenner was dyslexic. "It made me different than everybody else," says Jenner. "There was always that inferior dyslexic kid living inside me that always thought everybody else was better. But if I had not been dyslexic, I would not have had to prove myself, and I would have been average."

Sports saved Jenner's life. But it also put him in extremely high-pressure situations that he had to learn to overcome.

"When you set out to do anything," says Jenner, "whether it's to win an Olympic gold medal, or to build a business, or to do something that's going to improve your life, there's a risk involved. There's a lot of fear. So first you have to realize that you're going to be scared. It's part of the process.

"When I was at the Olympic games, my adrenal glands were the size of basketballs. That adrenaline was pumping like crazy. Fear is a great motivating factor. So it's the person who can overcome obstacles, know that fear is part of the process and make it work for him, who is going to come out ahead."

Many people believe that those who are successful have never known fear, have never had to struggle. This book gives people proof that success does not come easy; that you're not going to achieve your dreams by winning the lottery. Even the most successful have felt incredible anxiety, and have failed hundreds of times. They have made mistakes large and small. Mistakes are inevitable— but everyone can learn to stop those mistakes (and the fear of making them) from becoming barriers to a completed life.

As you read this book you will:

- Learn how to fail wisely;
- Readjust your thinking and take a new view of hardship and adversity;
- Learn from examples of ordinary people who became extraordinary and achieved extraordinary results—both despite and because of the obstacles they had to overcome; and
- Discover practical, action-oriented steps to achieve your desired goals and fulfill your dreams.

THE DIAMOND DIFFERENCE

It is not the adversities that successful people experience that make them shine, it is the valuable lessons they learn from overcoming obstacles, from rising to a challenge, from bouncing back from disappointment and failure.

What I learned from my own experience and extensive research, from the people I interviewed for *Diamond in the Rough*, and from the dozens of people I interviewed for this book, is that nothing is accomplished without some kind of challenge.

Everyone goes through rough times. Those who don't cope well with adversity get pulled down by its undertow and don't have the skills to swim back to shore. Not only that, they repeatedly enter the same waters, in the same spot, and are surprised when the undertow catches them again.

Successful people, too, have been caught by the undertow of adversity. But they learn from their experience. They don't enter the same waters again. But if they should somehow get swept under once more, they use skills they learned from their first experience to guide them back to solid ground.

That's what this book is about. The exciting adventure you're about to undertake as you read it will let you in on stories from people who have had amazing adventures of their own. People like Buddy Lazier, who won the Indianapolis 500 just a few short weeks after crashing his car against a wall at 180 miles per hour and breaking his back in sixteen places. People like Bruce Jenner and Carrie Graves, Olympic athletes who overcame great odds to win the gold. Or 1986 world champion Mets pitcher Ed Hearn, who had to give up the game—and almost took his life—when not one, not two, but three life-threatening illnesses changed his whole world. You'll hear from comedians such as Robert Schimmel about the constant rejection and failure they faced early on, and how determination and humor pulled them through.

I have tried, through relating my own experiences and through the experiences of all the people in this book, to get to the truth as best I can. No one will ever know the absolute truth, or the one right way to live our lives. In fact, the more we find out, the more we realize how much there is yet to learn. That is why there are so many viewpoints included here.

All these viewpoints, however, point to the same conclusion: Adversity is life's greatest teacher.

DARK ENOUGH TO SEE THE STARS

The great poet Ralph Waldo Emerson once wrote, "When it is dark enough, you can see the stars."

Truth is only discovered in times of difficulty. Courage and self-awareness blossom and grow the most when times are the roughest. When adversity strikes, it often feels like we are plunged into a dark void from which we will never emerge. But often when things are the darkest, the stars come out and shine their light upon us so that we can see the path before us.

That is what happened to Jo Jerman, vice-president of field support of Merck & Company, Inc. She heads the company's most successful regional division. Today, everyone regards Jerman as a success. But this wasn't always the case.

At the age of twenty-two, Jerman entered a marriage that lasted only eleven months. She was the first person in her family to be divorced, and everyone she knew considered this to be a great failure on her part. Not only had the marriage ended, but Jerman's ex had run up an enormous amount of debt and left her destitute. She was soon working three jobs and hardly able to make ends meet.

"But," says Jerman today, "what I learned at that relatively early age is that adversity is what teaches us about ourselves. That's when you become who you are. It's character-defining."

During this dark period of her life, Jerman was offered a job as a sales representative. "I was totally convinced I couldn't do it," she says. "Especially when I found out it meant moving away from home. I was scared, but I also knew this was my new beginning. It was a moment of decision—either I make this work, or I give up on everything."

Jerman believes that one of the reasons it's sometimes difficult to cope during rough times is that adversity challenges us to change, and that it is part of our human nature to resist change.

"One of the most important aspects of adversity," says Jerman, "is that it makes you feel so uncomfortable that you have no choice but to reexamine what you're doing and why you're doing it."

"Not many people are willing to give failure a second opportunity. They fail once and it's all over. The bitter pill of failure . . . is often more than people can handle. . . . If you're willing to accept failure and learn from it, if you're willing to consider failure as a blessing in disguise and bounce back, you've got the potential harnessing of one of the powerful success forces."

—JOSEPH SUGARMAN

LEARNING TO FOCUS

Reexamining what you're doing and why you're doing it is critically important in the process of coping with adversity. However, even extensive analysis will do you no good unless it's followed by action. We are at our worst and most desperate when we feel that everything is out of our control; that there is nothing we can *do* to help ourselves.

But there is something you can do. There is a tool you can use to help you regain the control you need. That tool is called FOCUS, and the next five chapters of this book are dedicated to the five facets of FOCUS:

- **F**oresight and **F**aith
- **O**rganization

- ◆ Concentrated Effort and **C**ourage
- ◆ **U**nderstanding
- ◆ **S**eeding and **S**ervice

FORESIGHT AND FAITH

"You see things, and you say, 'Why?' But I dream things that never were; and I say, 'Why not?' "

—GEORGE BERNARD SHAW

Before you can take any effective action, you must have a clear idea of where you want to go, and believe that you are going to get there. When you visualize yourself in a successful situation, you create a positive picture in your mind. If that picture is vivid enough, you can overcome any obstacles that may be in your way.

This combination of foresight and faith can create miracles. It is what keeps people going when everything around them begins to crumble and fall. What we see of a person is like the tip of an iceberg; their real strength and support, their vision and their belief, lie beneath the surface.

Comedian Bobby Collins, host of the VH1 hit series "Stand Up Spotlight," whom *The New York Times* called "the most natural comedian working today," grew up in poverty in lower Manhattan. He describes his family as "dysfunctional deluxe." Early on, Collins set goals for himself. He wanted a better life and he held on to his dreams of moving up and out. His faith helped him get there.

"What I use to guide me is this: I put God first, I put my family second, I put my career third," he says. "If I find that I put my career

12

over my family or my family over God, I always have to go back to where I got off track. I keep the balance alive. Sometimes my career is going real well, but am I taking care of my family the right way? Spiritually, am I following my path? Am I venturing off? You leave God out, you're not going to get there. If you have God in your life, if you take care of your family, if you follow your career and work hard, what goes around comes around.

"God makes things simple. Man complicates them. I keep things simple in my comedy and it seems to work. So I must be doing something right."

ORGANIZATION

"We have time enough if we will but use it aright."
—JOHANN WOLFGANG VON GOETHE

Foresight and faith can take you a long way toward changing your attitude about adversity. Many of us have dreams and visions of what we'd like our future to be. However, as long as they remain dreams and visions with no foundation in reality, there is very little chance of these dreams coming true. In order to transform a wish into a reality, you must begin to set your goals down in writing, and to break them down into small, tangible steps that can be achieved one at a time.

The most successful people know that nothing is ever achieved in one giant leap. It's the tiny steps you take, one by one, that help you reach your destination.

The chapter on organization will provide you with some of the best techniques you'll ever find for setting goals and carrying them out, in ways that make you feel comfortable and confident. You'll also find out how setting goals and making plans can help you through the greatest adversities. It is feelings of helplessness that lead to feelings of hopelessness. Once you begin to make practical, tangible plans for your future, that future can become a reality.

CONCENTRATED EFFORT AND COURAGE

"If we did all the things we are capable of doing, we would literally astound ourselves."

—THOMAS A. EDISON

Now you have a clear vision of where you want to go, a belief that you can get there, and step-by-step goals to guide you toward your objective. Once those three elements are in place, the real work begins. When we look at successful people, we usually see only the end result of their blood, sweat, and tears. We don't see the hours and hours of preparation and hard work that went into their success.

Everything tastes better with more effort in it. Which tastes better, a fast-food burger or a finely cooked steak? A meal on-the-go or dinner cooked at home? Microwaved leftovers or a gourmet five-course meal? Which meal will stay in your memory longer? There is no need to go out looking for obstacles and difficulties, but they do add spice to life. When you cut and chop and cook and simmer, the meal tastes all the more delicious because of the work that went into it. When you've worked really hard to attain a goal, the satisfaction is even sweeter because you know how much effort went before.

There is a basic truth of life that says what you put into it is what you get back. The rewards you get out of any endeavor depend on the amount of effort you put into it. Sometimes we're afraid of working hard, because we're afraid we won't get the reward in the end. Rewards are sometimes long in coming, but they do come. Most people who don't achieve as much as they want to in life don't fall short because of lack of ability, but because they gave up too soon. Those who do achieve know that it is only concentrated, focused effort that will produce results.

Nowhere is this more evident than in the martial arts, especially the practice of kung fu—which literally means the art of accomplishment through effort. Kung fu masters practice their amazing feats for years and years, gaining their expertise day by day in the tiniest of increments. They know they will fail many, many times, yet they keep going. In the chapter on concentrated effort and courage, we will explore some of their methods, and how applying these concepts can help you reach any destination, no matter how far away or how difficult the path.

Concentrated effort is the secret behind everyone's success. But there is another **C** that goes along with concentrated effort, and that is **C**ourage.

"Courage is resistance to fear, mastery of fear—not absence of fear."
—Mark Twain

Nothing of importance is gained without risk. It takes courage to go after a dream while dealing with the day-to-day realities of having to survive in our sometimes harsh world. Courage does not mean ignoring those day-to-day realities, nor does it mean taking foolhardy risks that might endanger ourselves or our families. Courage does mean taking carefully evaluated risks, facing the fears that may be holding us back, and accepting the inescapable fact that obstacles and setbacks are not failures—they are simply a part of life.

Most high achievers understand the relationship between risk and reality. Robert D. Ballard, an undersea explorer and director of the Center for Marine Exploration at the Woods Hole Oceanographic Institute, has led or participated in more than one hundred deep-sea explorations. He has visited the *Titanic* and discovered the German battleship *Bismarck*. From an early age, he dreamed of ocean adventures. He wrote in a commencement speech for the Worcester Polytechnic Institute (from a collection called *Hold Fast Your Dreams*, compiled by Carrie Bokyo and Kimberly Colen) that in every adventure you take in life, you must be prepared to fail:

For no quest is worth pursuing that does not require you to pass many tests, take numerous risks. . . . Every major adventure I have been on over the years has tested me severely. . . . I have lived through countless storms at sea. Winds over one hundred miles an hour, swells reaching fifty feet. And when I thought I could not last another minute, the winds dropped off, the seas flattened, and the blue sky appeared and my quest was reached.

UNDERSTANDING

There are two aspects to understanding in FOCUS. The first is comprehending why it is we *don't* do the things we dream of doing. One of the main reasons is fear. To most people, fear is a barrier, an impenetrable wall that stands between them and the fulfillment of their lifelong desires. It is a powerful emotion that can override our self-confidence, deceive us into believing we cannot do the things of which we are capable, and convince us that our dreams of achievement and success are simply impossible.

But dreams don't know they're impossible. It isn't until we over-analyze them, tear them to shreds, conjure up every negative possibility, and let fear rule our hearts that we take our large dreams and make them small. We see obstacles, real and imagined, everywhere in front of us. The fear of failure stops us from moving ahead, and our brightest dreams slowly fade and slip away.

It's as if there's an imaginary line in front of us, blocking our way. Some people are content to stay behind the line, settling for what life gives them instead of what they want out of life. The fewer risks you take in life, the thicker this line grows, until it becomes an unscalable wall. What is this imaginary line that blocks so many people from getting what they want? How can we step across it and keep moving forward? The chapter on understanding will explore various small steps anyone can take to cross the line before it becomes a barrier. It will also contain stories, anecdotes, and quotes from people who successfully made (and are constantly making) that leap.

The second aspect of understanding in FOCUS is gathering all the information you can about the subject in which you are interested. One of the most common excuses we have for not moving toward our dreams is "I don't know how to do that!" In today's world, however, with the huge variety of resources available to us, there is no excuse for this kind of excuse. There are bookstores and libraries full of information on every known subject; there is the Internet, which gives us access to information from around the world; and, most important, there are those people who have gone before us, most of whom are more than willing to share their insights and experiences.

I go through the understanding process every day as I try to develop my television show, market books to new industries, develop an audio magazine, and market sales, management, and motivational seminars to various organizations. For every project I'm working on, I try to contact as many people within that industry as I can, people who have many different responsibilities. When I collect all their information, I have a much better overview of the industry, and I can move forward with a confidence I didn't have before.

When I first started trying to get a television show on the air, I didn't know very much about the process involved. I've watched TV, and I've been a guest on numerous programs. But that doesn't mean I have specific knowledge of the way things are done in TV-land.

So I've been talking to as many people as I've been able to find who have experience in the television industry. So far, I've spoken to several producers, to someone who syndicates television programs, someone who sells advertising time for several cable stations, and to the CEO of a corporation that has underwritten a variety of programs. Not every person I've spoken to has direct knowledge of how to get a program on the air. But they all have valuable information about the industry itself.

What I'm trying to do is collect as much information as I can so that I can make intelligent decisions about how, when, and where to pursue my dream. Every time I get a new piece of information, my vision of the dream becomes clearer, and I am able to see a bigger picture. Understanding builds my confidence, which strengthens my faith. Understanding also tells me where I need to concentrate my efforts and what steps I need to take next to achieve my goal.

SEEDING AND SERVICE

"You can't live a perfect day without doing something for someone who will never be able to repay you."

—JOHN WOODEN

There is another phenomenon that occurs when I set out to talk to as many people as I can in the television industry. I am planting seeds for my future. Every person with whom I speak is a potential connection. Not every person will be able to help me reach my goal, but you never know. And you never know whom that person knows, or might meet in the future. You have to be planting your seeds all the time, because you never know which ones will bear the most fruit.

It is in times of adversity that seeding is often most important. If you lose your job, you can't just sit around the house and wait for someone to offer you a new one. If you lose a major client and your business is in danger of folding, you can't sit at your desk and wait for the phone to ring. If you suffer a major setback, you must face it head-on and start taking actions that will get you back on track.

The second **S** in FOCUS stands for service, which means giving back to others. When you ask high achievers to define success, you'll hear all kinds of answers, such as former Senator Bill Bradley's "maximizing the potential that God gave you for excellence;" ABC news correspondent Ann Compton's "a successful person is someone who does what he or she desires to do, and does it very well with quiet patience and determination;" or coauthor of *Chicken Soup for the Soul* Jack Canfield's "I think success ultimately is learning. When I learn and grow, I'm being successful." These definitions have one thing in common. They don't mention money, fame, or worldly goods. They talk about personal values, inner resources, and doing something worthwhile with your life. No one will deny that money is important, but it usually comes as a by-product of other achievements.

Take for instance Arthur Fry, the inventor of the Post-it Note. Everyone thinks he became a billionaire as a result of his efforts. He didn't. He was working for 3M at the time, and the profits were shared by all the employees & stockholders. Without the facilities and technology that 3M invested in the project, Fry would never have been able to achieve his goal. All he ever wanted was enough money to care for his family and to live comfortably. His motivation was not money, but to have the time and resources to come up with such creative inventions as the Post-it Note. He received no bonus, but he was promoted to a job with greater freedom, autonomy, challenge, responsibility, visibility, respect, and a good salary.

Wealth is not always the best indicator of success. I consider my father to be one of the most successful people I know, and he is not a millionaire. He was an art teacher for many years, and he loved what he did. Not only that, his students loved him. He is still getting calls from students he taught twenty years ago, thanking him for his enthusiasm and encouragement. That is what I call a great measure of success.

Life is not meant to be lived selfishly. The true key to living a successful life is to turn the focus from "how can I help myself" to "what can I do for others." Many years ago, William H. Danforth wrote a little book called *I Dare You*. In it he said, "Catch a passion for helping others and a richer life will come back to you." Whenever you find yourself off track, recognize that your center of focus is turned inward, toward yourself. As soon as you turn yourself around, everything will come back to you tenfold when you focus on helping others. The more you can impact other people's lives for the better, the greater your success becomes.

Musician and composer Billy Joel put it this way in a 1991 commencement address to Fairfield University (from *Hold Fast Your Dreams*):

> *I am not quite sure how one measures service. . . . However, if you do what you can, when you can, and sometimes when you cannot, perhaps that is enough. I would ask you to understand that the greatest service you can do for others is to fulfill your own heart's desires and become the best you can be for yourselves. Even though you will fall down and foul up and make mistakes as I have—as everyone does— you will make this world a better place if you can bring to it your own*

unique and individual excellence and quality and originality. . . . This
is the greatest service you can render to your community and others.

If you follow the five steps of FOCUS, which will be covered in depth in the next five chapters, you can get through any adversity, large or small.

When I interviewed Heavyweight Boxing Champion Evander Holyfield one week before his first winning bout with Mike Tyson, we talked about another fight where Holyfield ran into some unusual adversity. He was just about to land a knockout punch against Riddick Bowe when out of the blue (literally) a parachuter dropped right into the ring. The fight was stopped, and the boxers had to begin again twenty minutes later. I asked Holyfield how he was able to go on under such adverse conditions.

"Well, I felt that I came too far to let any kind of interruption take my mind off the event and make me lose focus," Holyfield told me. "I believe that in life the difference between winners and losers is focus: who can keep their focus longer. I prayed to be able to keep my focus. I was able to do that, and that's how I was able to win the match."

IT ALL DEPENDS ON HOW YOU LOOK AT IT

Recently, I read a story of two young boys who grew up in a broken home, abused by an alcoholic father. Eventually, they moved away from home and led separate lives. Years later, they both participated in a study of people who had grown up in alcoholic homes. One of the boys had become a successful businessman who never drank. His brother had grown up to be an alcoholic, now in desperate straits. The psychologist who was conducting the study asked each brother why he had ended up the way he did. Each one of them answered, "What else would you expect when you have a father like mine?"

This story proves that suffering has two paths. You can let adversity pull you down, or you can use it as a life force to spur you on to great accomplishments. It's your interpretation, your perspective on your circumstances, that determines which road you take. You can control how you react to adversity. That doesn't mean you can ignore it, or that you need to repress your emotions. You can't look at a tragic event while it is happening and say, "Oh, well, I'm sure there's a lesson here somewhere." Some people bounce back quicker than others. But we all have a choice to make, and it has been proven over and over again that it is not what happens to us in life that counts, but what we choose to do about it.

For some people, this is a lesson learned early. Many children who have been abused grow up to lead troubled lives. But there are others who grow up to be healthy individuals and upstanding citizens. For fifteen years, James Redfield (whose book *The Celestine Prophecy* was on *The New York Times* best-seller list for 140 weeks and was the best-selling American book worldwide for 1995 and 1996) was a therapist for emotionally challenged adolescents.

"What I learned from these kids is that it's all a matter of interpretation," says Redfield. "You take young people who have been abused early in their lives. The first thing they have to deal with is this negative trauma and the negative outlook that comes from that trauma. It's very difficult when you're abused early on to think that the world is a good place again—that there are positive events around the corner, that there are positive things that can happen and opportunities waiting. It's difficult to get back into that positive frame of mind."

But, according to Redfield, there were kids who could do that, who could stop the acting out that comes from the trauma, who could take responsibility for their own lives and find something to get inspired about. "The kids who went through those steps could then start to expect positive opportunities and positive events," he says. "As soon as they had that expectation, then they began to find those positive events in their lives.

Redfield also found this lesson became important to him in his own life. "I went through this process myself," he says. "I hit a lot of dead ends in writing *Celestine*. Brick walls. Funding that I thought I had that suddenly dried up. A whole section of the book I realized I needed to redo at the last minute. I kept hitting dead ends, one after another, until I found the way to interpret each one positively. I realized, just like those kids had to do, that we have to find a way to interpret events in our lives positively, and find the lesson and the message. Once we try to find the positive, then we learn to expect the positive, and doors begin to open all through our lives."

THREE STRIKES DON'T COUNT YOU OUT

If ever there was a story about finding the positives that come out of terrible adversity, it is Ed Hearn's. In 1986, Hearn was a member of the New York Mets world champion baseball team, and he thought all his dreams had come true. The following spring, he was traded to the Kansas City Royals for pitcher David Cone. Two weeks into his Kansas City season, he sustained a shoulder injury that took total reconstructive surgery and three years to battle. By 1991, Hearn realized that his baseball career was over.

But that wasn't all. Three months after he left baseball, he was diagnosed with three serious health problems. One was a condition called hypo gamma globulin anemia, which requires a $3,000 IV treatment each month. The second was sleep apnea, which means he stops breathing during sleep and now goes to bed attached to a breathing machine each night. The third, and most serious of all, was that he needed an immediate kidney transplant. Since 1992, Hearn has taken $40,000 worth of medication each year, and will continue to do so for the rest of his life.

One day in 1993, Hearn reached his lowest point. He went down to the basement of his home, picked up a .357 Magnum, and put a bullet in one of the chambers. He sat on a bench and contemplated taking his own life. He thought long and hard about it, and realized that "deep deep down" he was not a quitter.

There were three factors that turned things around for Hearn.

"Number one," he says, "I recognized that I had a problem. I couldn't just keep wallowing around in self-pity. I had to do something. Nobody was going to do it for me. So I went and got psychiatric help. He gave me therapy, and some medication that really helped me.

"The second thing I did to help myself: I had always heard that if you fill your mind with positive things, you can actually change your thought process. So I became a tape junky. I listened to Earl Nightingale and all the big motivational speakers. I listened every time I drove my car; I fell asleep every night listening to them. After a while, these things became a part of me. It began to lift my spirits, and I began to think of things a little more positively.

"Finally, the third thing that really gave me a little hope, was when I was invited to speak to a Rotary Club in Kansas City by a former Chiefs player. I went and did the old forty-minute 'rubber chicken' talk. I really didn't want to go. I was still depressed. But my buddy insisted. After the speech a man came up to me, and said he was the president of a national speaker's bureau. He gave me his card and he said, 'You have a great story and you tell it well. Corporate America will pay you to do this because so many people are facing challenges in today's world.' That day I went home and told my wife, 'I don't know what all this is about, why I went through all this crap. But today, a man told me I might be able to have a big impact on a lot of people.' "

These days, Hearn travels all over the country speaking to corporations, associations, and youth groups. "Today, I honestly say I look forward to speaking more than I used to look forward to playing in major league ball games," says Hearn. It was the three steps he took that saved his life. First, he took action. He went to see someone who could really give him the help he needed. The second step was to listen to positive ideas. The third, most critical step was to realize how he could impact other people's lives. As Zig Ziglar once said, "You can get anything you want in this life if you help enough other people get what they want."

"That's the theme by which I live my life," says Hearn. "When

I go out and speak today, certainly I get paid nicely, but some of the greatest paychecks are the emotional paychecks I get when people come up to me afterwards and say, 'I didn't want to come to this meeting. It was mandatory. We have these things all the time, they're so boring. But I'm glad I came today because you really touched me. You had a tremendous impact on my life today.' It doesn't get any better than that. If I never had the shoulder injury, if I'd never gotten sick, I never would have had the opportunity to do what I'm doing today. I could have played twenty years in the big leagues and not have had the opportunity to impact the lives that I do today from the speaking platform. Fire purifies gold. Heat tempers steel. Adversity builds character—if you face it with the right attitude. Here's the big number one point that I always make to people: You've got to put your life, and the challenges you face into the proper perspective. The world we live in today is a world in which we're running here, running there, trying to keep up with the Joneses. When little things get in our way, they become major stumbling blocks. But when we put things in perspective, we realize they're only little anthills we trip over. Then we get back up again and go on with our lives."

Adversity is what you make of it. It is often a blessing in disguise. It is the one part of life that can teach us more than any other.

The goal of this book is to let you know that you can do anything you want to do, but you're going to hit some obstacles and make some mistakes along the way. Most of us live in fear of making mistakes; we don't want anyone to know we've made them, and often can't face them ourselves. But mistakes are part of human nature and part of our learning process.

When you're learning to play basketball, for example, you spend a lot of time practicing shots. Everyone, even the pros, misses a lot of shots. But if you stop after you miss, study your form and your position, and ask yourself, "Why didn't that shot work?" and "What can I do next time to improve?" you're bound to start making a few. This applies to everything in life. If you never pick up that ball, make that phone call, go to that interview, take that risk—you'll never have a shot at making your dream come true. Sometimes you've got to learn what you can't do before you can learn what you can do.

"Both science and life are trial-and-error processes," says scientist and inventor Art Fry. "It's like the children's game of red-hot. A friend thinks about an object in his mind and you're supposed to find it. He says, 'Nope, you're getting colder, colder, cold, warm, warmer, red-hot!' And finally you find what you're looking for.

"You've got to look at failure as an important ingredient for success. The educational process of what does and doesn't work is very valuable."

Each and every one of us has great potential within. We are diamonds under pressure, and we can let that pressure destroy us, or allow it to force the best of us to rise to the surface. It is up to each and every one of us to make that choice.

two

Foresight
and Faith

SEVERAL YEARS AGO, Robert Schimmel was managing a stereo store in Scottsdale, Arizona. He went out to Los Angeles to visit his sister, and while he was there they went to a comedy club. On stage were people like Jay Leno, Jerry Seinfeld, Larry Miller, and George Wallace. Schimmel's sister said, "You're as funny as these guys! Why don't you try comedy?" Schimmel answered, "I couldn't do that."

They came back later in the week on amateur night. Although Schimmel didn't know it, his sister had put his name on the list of performers. They were sitting in the audience when the announcer said, "And now for our next comic, Robert Schimmel!"

Schimmel went up on stage and talked about his parents for two minutes. The audience laughed. The owner of the club came over and said, "You can work here whenever you want. Just call me up and I'll give you a spot."

That's when Robert Schimmel began to see himself as a comedian. He pictured himself on stage, right next to Leno and Seinfeld. So he went back to Arizona and told his wife of his dream. He convinced her (although she thought he was crazy) to move to L.A., so they put the house up for sale, packed all their things in a U-Haul, and drove off to sunny California.

Without even stopping at his sister's house, Schimmel made straight for the club that had promised him employment, so he could show it to his wife. When they got there, all that was left was smoldering embers. It had burned down the night before. But Schimmel would not give up on his dream.

"After I got up on that stage the first time, I knew I had to come back to L.A. and make a go of this. It was all I thought about. When I got here and the club was destroyed, I got a job selling stereo equipment and went to every amateur night I could find. I had to do it. My vision was so clear I felt like I had no choice. If you bet on yourself like that, there's more to win than if you play it safe and let yourself be afraid of failure. You have to have a plan, and you have to go for it."

Today, Robert Schimmel appears with those comedians he so admired; he was recently named Comic of the Year by the *Las Vegas Review Journal* and his newest CD was featured in *Time* magazine. All because he had a vision of his future that he wouldn't give up, no matter what obstacles presented themselves to him.

As we go along in our day-to-day existence making plans, making decisions, making choices, there is one important concept to remember: We are the architects of our lives. It is the vision that we create, the picture we hold up before us, that determines where we end up. What we can imagine ourselves to be becomes the foundation for the metamorphosis of every one of our dreams—from wish into reality.

The one thing that all great achievers—no matter what their field or occupation—have in common is the ability to visualize their dreams. They have a clear, focused picture of their destination, and it is this clear picture they strive toward no matter what obstacles may appear before them. That doesn't mean their dreams always come true, or turn out 100 percent the way they dreamed them. Nobody can actually predict the future. Sometimes these high achievers had to restructure their visions, make compromises, open their minds to the surprises life throws at all of us from time to time.

But they never lost their ability to sustain a positive vision of the future, and the belief that the vision would one day become a reality. Foresight and faith. The two go hand in hand—*must* go hand in hand. Some people paint pictures in their minds all the time. They have wonderful, creative ideas, one after another. And they just let them go, let them burst in the air like bubbles from a jar. "They're only dreams," they tell themselves. They don't believe they can ever be more than that.

High achievers don't let the bubbles burst so easily. They let them float around for a long time, study them from every angle, and watch them grow and expand. They nurture their dreams. They believe in them. Faith is what pulls them forward and makes them strong. Dreams and visions are innately fragile, and unless they are buoyed up by faith, they are just sprinkles in the air that are going to fall like dust.

> *"The mind is the limit. As long as the mind can envision the fact that you can do something, you can do it—as long as you really believe 100 percent."*
>
> —ARNOLD SCHWARZENEGGER

BUILDING A MENTAL MODEL

I said earlier that we are the architects of our own lives. How do architects do their job? First, they have a vision. They think about the building. They form a mental picture of just what the building will look like when it's completed. Then they begin asking themselves questions that will bring their picture into a clearer focus.

Where is the building going to be located? What is its intended function? What are the other buildings in the area like, and how will this one fit into the community? What is it going to look like? What will it be built out of? How much money will it take to complete the project? How long will it take?

That is how they make their vision a reality. As they answer their own questions, they discover how they can make the building work, or where they need to revise their plans. From a vague idea comes a concrete reality.

Athletes and artists use visualization all the time. When Ed Hearn was playing ball, he would spend time alone before the game to visualize the opposing pitcher and replay in his mind the types of pitches this man would throw. Then he would visualize himself hitting pitch after pitch on a line drive. Many Olympic athletes have described how they run every race or dive every dive mentally long before they hit the track or the pool.

Michelangelo studied his stones long before he began to sculpt. He saw what was hiding beneath the surface. When he was sculpting his famous David, he said that he looked at the stone and then cut away everything that wasn't David. His vision was that clear. The artist Matisse was once photographed in slow motion. The film showed that before every brush stroke Matisse studied the canvas, then as his hand approached the easel, he would practice the actual brush stroke in midair and visualize what it would be before putting it on the canvas, and then finally, the brush would touch the canvas and paint the vision in Matisse's mind. This visualization instinct was so strong and ingrained that Matisse himself was not even aware that he did it until he saw the film in slow motion.

NEGATIVE FORESIGHT

We actually use our powers of visualization all the time. Unfortunately, however, we usually utilize our "negative foresight." We anticipate our failures before they happen. We create self-fulfilling prophecies; we convince ourselves we're going to fail and so we do.

The funny thing is that most of us have no trouble believing in this negative foresight. Our lack of self-confidence convinces us that failure is the most probable outcome of any endeavor. It's easy to think negatively about the future and how things will go wrong.

Experience tells us that to get a success you usually have to go through many failures. So why not just expect the failure to begin with? Why do people find it easier to believe in the power of negative thinking than in the power of positive thought? Why is it easier to visualize failure than success? One reason is that people tend to create an image that they feel comfortable with. Imagining that you'll be successful, and then going after that success, is, after all, risky business. There is very little risk involved in saying, "This is not going to turn out well," and then proving yourself right.

Another reason is that we are programmed early in life to believe that things will turn out badly. People do not always encourage us when we want to try something new and different. They tell us things like "I had a cousin who tried that once, and look what happened to her!" Or "There's so much competition out there, you'll never make it." Very rarely do you find someone who will say, "So you're taking a risk! That's wonderful. Go out there and have fun, and I'm sure you'll be a success!"

It is easy to believe these negative people. We have all heard the saying "The higher you climb, the harder the fall." We fear there is a price for success we may not be willing to pay. We are raised on stories of starving artists, unappreciated in their lifetimes, sacrificing everything for their chance at success. We learn that money is evil, and that fame destroys us. With these kinds of stories filling our heads, it's amazing that anyone tries to accomplish anything at all.

Yet there is something in the human spirit that won't allow us to just give up. If every dreamer in history had listened to the naysayers around him or her, humankind would not be where it is today. Winston Churchill, who was a failure at school, failed his way through his entire career, from the time he was not promoted higher than a junior cavalry officer, through his rise to chancellor of the exchequer, where he precipitated a world money crisis. Albert Einstein failed algebra. Franklin Delano Roosevelt was judged by most of his contemporaries to be a mediocre lightweight; even his mother was known to be outspoken about her son's shortcomings. Vincent Van Gogh sold only one painting in his entire lifetime, and the emperor for whom Wolfgang Amadeus Mozart composed once criticized his operas saying they had "too many notes."

"Men do not attract that which they want, but that which they are. Their whims, fancies, and ambitions are thwarted at every step, but their innermost thoughts and desires are fed with their own food, be it foul or clean. The 'divinity that shapes our ends' is in ourselves; it is our very self. Man is manacled only by himself: Thought and actions are the jailers of Fate—they imprison, being base; they are also the angels of Freedom—they liberate, being noble. Not what he wishes and prays for does a man get, but what he justly earns. His wishes and prayers are only gratified and answered when they harmonize with his thoughts and actions."

—JAMES ALLEN, *AS A MAN THINKETH*

VISIONARY TOOLS

A vision is created out of imagination. But it needs fuel to sustain itself. Left alone, a vision is likely to disappear, or become so vague that we can hardly remember what we meant it to be in the first place. The old adage "Use it or lose it" definitely applies here. A vision, once developed, needs to be nurtured and supported to be sustained. There are tools you can use to strengthen your vision and keep it focused and clear, and there are ways you can use your vision to spur you on to take action. Here are a few suggestions for using these visionary tools:

MAKE YOUR VISION REAL TO YOU.

Take it seriously. Weigh the pros and cons involved. Realize that the possibility for failure does exist, along with the chances for success. If you're not sure about your willingness to pursue your dreams, now is the time to find out. Realize, of course, that you don't have to give up everything you've currently got to go after your dreams. All you need to do is take one small step at a time.

Look to your past to shore up your future. Just as we've all had failures at some time in our lives, we've all had successes as well. Those past successes can serve as blueprints for future accomplishments. When the outcome of a particular endeavor seems questionable, you can increase your chances of success by remembering a positive outcome experienced in the past.

Carrie Graves is an Olympic gold-medal rower, currently coach of Northeastern University women's crew team. Despite all her training and practice races, Graves consistently experienced fear and doubt before important competitions. Then she learned a technique that helped her get through every race. She used visual imagery, remembering earlier successful races.

"I would think about winning the race, and what it would feel like," says Graves. "I would think about how the boat would feel, how hard I would pull, how well I have pulled in the past. I would think about how powerful and omnipotent being in the boat makes me feel."

Graves has been using this technique successfully for many years. "When I was younger, I would spend a lot of time thinking about past successes," she says. "As I got older and more experienced, all I had to do was start to think about a past race and immediately I could focus on winning. It took me about thirty seconds."

This technique can be applied to any type of activity. There doesn't have to be a direct correlation; a past success in any area can be used to give you confidence in any other area. Suppose you were a champion tennis star in college, but no longer play the game. You can still draw on useful images, remembering the mental and physical manifestations of winning a match, to help you succeed in any new field you enter.

Surround yourself with images of success. You don't have to rely on your imagination to help you visualize success. Construct visual reminders of your plans and goals and put them on your walls, or on your desk, or carry them in your purse or wallet (in the next chapter we'll talk more about the best ways to construct these plans and how best to keep them in front of you). Read about things that excite you. Watch the television and rent videos on subjects that interest you.

If you surround yourself with dull images, you'll think dull thoughts. If you surround yourself with images that are full of energy and have a special meaning to you, you'll naturally want to take actions that bring you closer to these images.

Surround yourself with people who are visionaries themselves. Alice Bredin is president of Bredin Business Information (a New York City–based consulting firm), a syndicated columnist, and author of *The Virtual Office Bible Handbook*. She deems herself an expert on adversity and failure, having gone through so much of it herself. She also believes that every time you fail, you bring yourself basically one step closer to reaching your goal.

"I look at it as a checklist," says Bredin. "You have to go through a certain amount of failure to get to the things you want to achieve in your life. Every time I fail, I think, This was a requisite to getting to my goal. Now that I've gotten that failure out of the way, I'm that much closer to reaching my goal."

Bredin attributes her attitude to "growing up and not having a whole lot." Her parents told her that if she wanted something, she had to go after it and get it, and that if she expected life to be really easy, then she was going to be in for a hard life. "Not that you should be negative and expect that things aren't going to go your way," adds Bredin. "But you have to expect a certain amount of hard times. My successes and failures have been about fifty-fifty— which, in my book, is basically success. Because failure only occurs if you give up and stop trying."

One way that Bredin surrounds herself with visionary people is to read biographies and autobiographies on a regular basis. "You find out that every single successful person has had all kinds of adversity, whether it's been in their personal life or their professional life," she says. "If I'm going through a particularly hard time or if I know that I'm likely to be encountering some failure, I just pick up one of these books, even though I've read it before, and read a few chapters. I find them really inspirational."

Bredin is also particularly careful about the company she keeps. "I surround myself with visionary kinds of people who are interested in talking about goals and big ideas, and who are doing really interesting things themselves," she says. "That keeps me focused on my goals. If you're not surrounded by people who are interested in hearing about your vision, then your vision is going to drop through the floorboards. If you're surrounded by people who are doing big things, they're going to be interested in hearing about the big things you're doing. The more you talk about your vision, the more real it becomes, and the more likely you are to accomplish your goals."

Visualize your own success. Just as you can use images of past success to help you accomplish a goal, you can imagine your future success as well. The definition of foresight is to be able to see something before it happens. Before you pick up a phone to make an important call, think about what you want to say. Determine the goal of the call and what you want it to accomplish. Make a list of the questions you want to ask. Imagine yourself getting all your points across, and the other person responding positively. You can use this same technique for a sales call, a meeting with your boss, a job interview, or any event where you want to have a successful outcome.

You can also use visualization as a motivator. Everyone has certain material things they would like to acquire in their lives. There is nothing wrong with wanting things, as long as we don't let them become the entire focus of our lives. But sometimes, having visual reminders of the things we want makes us work harder to get them.

Carolyn Spargur is a top distributor with a well-known network marketing company. Spargur was a divorced mother of four, trying to raise her children on her own. She was working two jobs, and an extra one when one of her children needed braces. When she discovered network marketing, she was "trying to get out of things, not into things," she says. But by working hard, and totally believing in what she was doing, Spargur has become one of the most successful distributors in her organization.

One aid that Spargur uses is called a dream workboard. She goes through magazines, newspapers, and any other sources she can think of, and cuts out pictures of the things she would like to acquire within a specific time period. This is a project she used to take to meetings with her, to encourage other people to make their own workboards. "I thought I was doing it for other people," she says. "But it caught hold of my own mind, and I worked for it, and I made all of my goals."

What you're doing every time you use visualization as a tool is setting up the circuitry in your mind to attract success. Once this circuitry is in place, the incredible power of the human mind attracts a positive result. Even scientists can't explain this phenomenon but know that it works.

It's like the mysterious way the mind functions when something is on the tip of your tongue, but you just can't get it out. We've all had that experience of trying to remember the name of a person we used to know, or an actor in a film. You think and you think and you concentrate and you know that you know it and you want to say it . . . and nothing. It just won't come. Then, three hours later, in the middle of a conversation about something else entirely, you shout, "Audrey Hepburn!" Even though you haven't been consciously trying to think of the name, your subconscious continued the search.

The same powerful subconscious forces are at work when we use visualization. The subconscious keeps your vision intact even when you're not consciously aware of it. And, as long as the vision remains strong, the subconscious will keep directing you to take actions that will lead to making that vision a reality.

> *"[One] characteristic a leader must possess is objectivity. He must be someone who is constantly referring back to his mission when problems come up. Someone who makes all his decisions based not on what he had for breakfast or how he feels or whether he likes the person he's dealing with, but on whether it gets him closer to his vision or backs him off."*
>
> —WARREN BENNIS, AUTHOR OF *REINVENTING LEADERSHIP*

KEEPING THE FAITH

There is a catch to this "vision thing" of course (you knew there had to be a catch). The catch is that you have to believe in your vision 110 percent. You have to have faith. You have to know absolutely in your heart that your dream is a worthy one, that your vision is what you *really* want out of life, and that you are willing to work toward that goal. If any of these three components is missing, simply having a vision is not good enough.

And if that vision is strong enough, it can be communicated to others around you, who also come to believe in that dream. No matter how many obstacles are put in the way.

Ron Hemelgarn is president of Hemelgarn Racing, Inc. His team, led by driver Buddy Lazier, won the Indianapolis 500 in 1996. It was the realization of Hemelgarn's lifelong dream. But right up until the starting gun, it seemed as if 1996 would go down as one of the worst in Hemelgarn's personal and professional life.

Late in 1995, Stan Fox, one of Hemelgarn's drivers, was in one of the most horrifying crashes in the history of the Indianapolis Speedway. For many weeks, Fox was comatose, fighting for his life. Hundreds of thousands of dollars invested in the racing car were destroyed within a matter of seconds. Many people thought Hemelgarn Racing was done for.

In December of that year, Hemelgarn's father was diagnosed with leukemia and given only a few weeks to live. In January, with his father in the hospital, Hemelgarn went to Disney World to watch Buddy Lazier race his car. They led for the first twenty-nine laps, when a $10 bolt broke and put them out of the race.

A few weeks later, Hemelgarn and Lazier were getting ready to race in Phoenix, when Hemelgarn's father passed away. At home for the funeral, Hemelgarn got a phone call telling him that Lazier had crashed in Phoenix and broken his back in sixteen places. It could have been the end of both their dreams. But these men had so much faith and commitment to each other and to their goal, that two months later Lazier was back in the driver's seat.

However, racing is a team sport, and if the team is not behind a driver, the race is lost before it's begun. "You have to have a group of people who believe that they can win," says Hemelgarn, "and that they can prepare the finest race car on the track on a given day. That team has to believe in the driver, and believe that he can win the race."

During a team meeting the night before Lazier's first race after the crash, Hemelgarn told his crew, "The only thing that will ever beat us is ourselves—if we allow ourselves to get down, or doubt ourselves one bit. If one team player thinks we cannot win this race, we could lose." He spent the next three hours with his team, planning the race out step by step.

For Buddy Lazier, racing in the Indy was a test of his faith. "During the race in Phoenix, going down the back straightaway, the rear wing came off. As the driver, I had no idea the rear wing just came off the car. I entered the corner, and for what appeared to be no reason at all, I crashed and hit the wall. It's very difficult to get that level of confidence back up." But it's always been Lazier's biggest dream to win the Indy 500, and he knew that in 1996 he had his best shot ever. "When you're focused on something like that," he says, "you don't let anything get in your way."

POSITIVE DREAMS

Ron Hemelgarn and Buddy Lazier were able to achieve their dreams because of their faith and their commitment to overcome any and all obstacles. We all have the capacity to believe that strongly in our dreams. James Redfield had great faith in *The Celestine Prophecy*, so much so that he originally published it himself, and traveled around the country introducing himself to bookstore clerks and buyers, asking them to stock his book. His faith paid off when the book began to sell by word of mouth that became so strong, Warner Books eventually bought the book and gave it major distribution.

When I interviewed Redfield on my radio show, I asked him what one piece of advice he felt was most important for our listeners. His answer was that everyone should begin with the vision that his or her most positive dreams can come true.

"Every one of us has a little voice inside, a little intuition, about what we would really want to do, about what our niche really is in this life, and how we can be most productive and make the greatest contribution," he said. "It may not always be clear. It may begin very nebulously. But we should all grab on to that dream, and know that anything we can visualize for ourselves can happen, as long as it comes from a place of love and positive contribution. As long as those two factors are there, then anything we can visualize has potential."

Those two factors are what ground us in life. They keep us stable, and keep us from crumbling when the winds of adversity try and blow us down. If you build your life on a foundation of ethics and integrity, you can handle the rough spots with grace and courage. Your choices become easier because you know there are certain lines you will not cross.

Suppose someone offered you $10 to do something you felt was wrong. It wouldn't be very difficult to turn down the offer. But suppose the amount were $10 million? How strong would your ethics be then?

Recently there was a story on the news about an armored car filled with hundreds of thousands of dollars in coins that overturned on a Florida highway. Citizens in the area rushed to the scene and began scooping up the cash and stuffing in their pockets. The next day, a ten-year-old child walked into the police department and returned 85 cents he had picked up off the road. It is not hard to imagine that this young man will grow up to be a success in life.

GUIDING PRINCIPLES

"Any path is only a path. There is no affront to yourself or others in dropping it if that is what your heart tells you to do. But your decision to keep on the path or to leave it must be free of fear and ambition. I warn you: look at every path closely and deliberately. . . . Then ask yourself and yourself alone one question. It is this: Does the path have a heart?. . . . If it does, then the path is good. If it doesn't, it is of no use."

—Carlos Castaneda

It is not enough to believe in your dreams if they leave you empty and unfulfilled. That is what happened to Norm Miller, Chairman of Interstate Batteries, the leading replacement battery manufacturer in North America, with $420 million in annual revenue. When he graduated from college, Miller thought about what he wanted from life. He wanted a pretty wife, a great job, to make a lot of money, have cars and a house and kids. By the time he was thirty-five, he had all those things. He was supposed to be happy. But there was an emptiness in his life.

"I had always been a big partier, a big drinker," says Miller. "I started drinking at age fourteen. Parties and fun were my whole life. Work was something I had to do to get all those things that I wanted. At thirty-five, I got busted by the police. I had been stopped for two Drinking While Intoxicateds before. I got stopped again. To make a long story short, I got out of it that night, and the police took me home. But the next morning I realized I was out of control.

"I thought my accomplishments and my things were going to make me happy. Then I realized that, like my father before me, I'd become an alcoholic. When this realization hit me I blurted out, 'God help me, I can't handle it.' God did it. He took away compulsion for drinking, and I discovered the Bible.

"When I went through the Bible, I noticed all these principles about how to treat people. One of which is to treat your neighbor as yourself. I began to try to treat people the way that I would want to be treated. We incorporated that into our business; we look out for the interests of everybody we deal with. I want you to understand we make mistakes and we foul up and we get selfish and greedy and all that. But our goal, the thing we come back to always, is to swap spots with the person and see what it would take to make them happy, instead of looking for the profit first and then letting everything else fall by the wayside."

It's much easier to make decisions in life if you have a guiding principal. Most top achievers do. Which is not to say they are always perfect, or never make mistakes. But even when they slip and fall, they soon return, stronger than ever, to their chosen path—whatever that path may be. Dreams don't have to be grandiose to be worthy. Your goal doesn't have to be to write the great American novel or discover the cure for cancer. Everyone has his or her own particular skills and talents. A landscaper's dream may be to beautify a neighborhood; a carpenter may aspire to build practical, sturdy furniture that people can live with for years to come. The dream itself doesn't matter, as long as it meets these criteria:

- It is beneficial to yourself and to those around you.
- It allows you to utilize your skills and talents.
- It is something you believe in so strongly that no adversity can keep you from pursuing it.

THE ATTITUDE OF FAITH

There's more to faith than just believing in yourself and in what you want to do. It's having a *passion* for what you do, a passion so strong that it makes you want to give it everything you've got, all the time. It is this passion that drives many of today's highest achievers.

You'd certainly have to put country superstar Barbara Mandrell in that category. She was the first artist ever to win two successive Country Music Association awards for Entertainer of the Year; she's a two-time CMA Female Vocalist of the Year winner; and she's won nine People's Choice awards, including the Living Legends award, which is only given to those in the industry who have had twenty-five years of consistent success.

Mandrell started at the age of eleven in Las Vegas, playing steel guitar and saxophone in a two-week engagement with Joe Mavis and Tex Ritter. She was extremely well received by the band as well as by the audience. But everyone suggested to her, "You gotta sing, too."

"So I said okay, and I just started singing," says Mandrell. She was able to do that because of the confidence instilled in her by her parents. "They taught me to say, 'I can do that. I know it sounds hard, I know it's scary. But I can do it,' " she says. She always remembers her father's advice about attitude. When she was a youngster, her father explained the relationship of attitude to success. "Suppose you were going to open a gas station," Mandrell says. "Suppose you go into it with the attitude, 'I'm going to start this business, but I don't know if I'm going to make it. I don't know if it will do any good.' You won't succeed. But if your attitude is 'I'm going to make this the best gas station anybody's ever been in, and it's going to be superb,' there's no way it won't succeed."

This example has stuck with Mandrell throughout the years. "And I do know from experience," she says, "that you can apply this to any field, any career, no matter where you are, no matter what you're doing. For instance, in music, even if you're just singing in church, if you're performing in a school play or for a local Moose or Elks club, it may seem like a very small venue. But you don't know who's there, you don't know who's watching you. You don't know what door will open if you're performing 100 percent."

Mandrell expects the most of her crew as well as herself. "I'm very demanding of myself and of my people," she says. "They're very loyal and I really love them. I have almost thirty men that work for me. And I like that. We're a very close-knit group. All of the crew, all of the cast. Everybody matters. It takes all of us to put it out there the way it should be for the people. Every time out, even when we're doing one-nighters, the show we're doing is the most important one ever. It could be our last—and I know that literally because of the tragic affair in my life ten years ago when I had a terrible car crash that almost ended my career.

"Every time you deliver a service to people, it could be the last time you do it. So every time has to be done with passion. Some people enjoy going to work, and some dread it. I think those that dread it are in the wrong profession."

Another superstar whose attitude has helped him get through life is Heavyweight Champion Evander Holyfield. His attitude and passion for life came from his mother, who taught him that he was "born to win."

"My mother told me that being born to win is all in your attitude, knowing who you're supposed to be. If you go out there and give your all, and never quit, you can reach that pinnacle."

You don't have to be a superstar to have a good attitude about life. But sometimes having a good attitude can save your life. Hal Becker has known extreme ups and downs in his life, and keeping a healthy attitude literally kept him alive.

After college, Becker had a hard time finding a job. He was finally hired by Xerox when he decided to do something he had never done before.

"I was always a rebel kid. But I decided that if this company is running a $100 million training complex, maybe they know something I don't know. So I decided to do exactly what they said. And

I followed their rules. The first year was all training. The second year I became the number one salesman in the country at Xerox, out of eleven thousand people."

Becker decided to take what he'd learned at Xerox and apply it to a company of his own. In December 1982 he started a company called Direct Opinions, with no customers, nothing but a business plan. He hired an office manager and started working from the second floor of his house.

In February of 1983, Becker was diagnosed with terminal cancer. Doctors told him he had a 30 percent chance of living. He was hospitalized for eight and a half months, going through experimental chemotherapy because there was no cure at that time.

"People ask me all the time, what cured you?" says Becker. "I say, two things. One, conventional medical practice saved my life. But what helped me get through the ordeal was a positive mental attitude. I vowed that since that experience, I would never let things get me down. I took pictures of myself when I was sick, when I weighed 83 pounds and had no hair. Now if I have a bad day, if I'm speaking at a seminar and someone in the audience is a jerk, I remember those pictures and say big deal, I'm alive.

"Every day is a bonus day for me. Do I plan for a future? Do I have six thousand free miles that maybe I'll use someday? Yeah. But every day, if I can't have fun, I don't want to do it."

Becker's positive mental attitude began when he was taught how to do "vision projection."

"When I get down or depressed, I picture myself on a boat, waterskiing, or taking part in sports around the country on a nice July or August evening," he says. "Let's say today is a really crappy day.

I just picture myself on a July night, it's about eleven o'clock. The fireflies are all around me. Or I'll picture myself in a little sports car driving through the park.

"I was up in Raleigh-Durham not long ago. I had to leave at seven in the morning for an all-day session. I got a flight back to Cleveland which got me back to my house at seven-thirty at night. I had enough time to go through the mail, go to the bathroom, get in the car, and drive four and a half hours to Cincinnati, because I had an all-day session the next day. Can I complain about that? Sure. But still I said, 'What if I take my favorite CDs with me? I'm gonna get in the car, crank it up, it's a pretty night. I'm gonna enjoy it.' I've got news for you. The ride was too short. I changed my attitude. When I got there I wasn't even that tired."

Holyfield, Mandrell, and Becker are examples of people who, backed by faith and passion, put 110 percent effort into whatever they do. Some people think that faith alone is enough—that if they believe strongly enough they don't have to take action.

That reminds me of a story told to me by very funny comedian Bobby Collins. There's a hurricane coming, and flood warnings on the TV and radio. The police come and knock on an old man's door, telling him they've come to help him evacuate before the flood. The old man says, "I have faith in God, He's going to take care of me. You can go on and leave my house alone." The floods begin, and another man knocks on the door and says, "Old man, grab your belongings and hop in my boat to safety." The man replies, "I have faith that God will take care of me. Go on to someone else."

The next thing you know the waters have risen and the old man is standing on his roof. A helicopter comes by and drops a rope. The old man shouts up to the pilot, "God will take care of me. Leave me alone." The helicopter leaves, and the man drowns.

When he meets God, he says angrily, "What happened? I thought you were going to take care of me?"

"What do you mean, what happened?" says God. "I sent you a policeman, a boat, and a helicopter!"

THE WAY OF THE WARRIOR

It is easy to talk about having a passion for what you do. But it is not always so easy to find. What do you do if you're not sure what your passion is? You can start by listing what Olympic gold medal winner Billy Mills calls "positive desires": positive, constructive things you're interested in pursuing. Do this with a partner. Make a list of twelve positive desires. Share them with your partner. Then eliminate six of them, and discuss the remaining six with your partner. Then eliminate three, keeping one long-range and two short-range desires. Have your partner do the same with his or her list, and support each other on these desires.

Billy Mills teaches this system to children on Indian reservations. It comes from a message about how to have his dreams come true that his father gave him when he was twelve. The message said, "The secret is to find your desires, know yourself, and succeed. With desire comes self-motivation, with self-motivation comes work, and with work comes success."

How do you know when you've found a positive desire? "Something happens inside of you," says Mills. "You unleash incredible passion. And it's the passion within you that motivates you." Mills didn't always have his own positive desires. This author of *Wokini: Your Personal Journey to Happiness and Understanding* had a movie based on his life called *Running Brave,* which starred Robby Benson.

"I was rejected for being mixed blood, half-Indian and half-white," Mills recalls. "The Lakota culture called me mixed blood, the White culture called me Indian. Neither of those two cultures allowed me to participate. I was a sophomore in college, on the 12th floor, totally confused and I was going to jump. Instead of jumping, I closed the window. I said that God had given me ability, the rest is up to me. I remembered some of the other advice my dad had given me, such as that my life is a gift to me from my creator, my God. What I do with my life is my gift back to God. I made the commitment that my gift would be pursuing excellence by following my positive desires."

Mills says that the ultimate goal in life is to unleash the passion within the positive desire. "When you do that you're willing to accept the defeats in life. They're not failures. All the while you're accepting defeat, you're willing to pursue excellence. Ultimately that pursuit of excellence takes you to a higher plateau."

Mills also challenges people to live their lives as warriors do. A warrior focuses his or her life in four areas:

1. *A warrior assumes self-responsibility.* As you become responsible for yourself, you reach out and help other people become responsible.

2. *A warrior humbles himself or herself to all creation.* We're no better or no less than the smallest living blade of grass. But as we find that balance of humility, we never lose sight of that pursuit of excellence that takes us to a higher plateau.

3. *A warrior learns the power of giving.* The first thing you learn to give is respect to yourself, so you can then respect your fellow man.

4. *A warrior takes responsibility, humility, and the power of giving, and centers it around his or her core of spirituality.* This is true whether the warrior is of the Jewish faith, the Christian faith, or Native American religion—whatever faith he or she might encounter.

FAITH IN THE QUIET TIMES

What is faith anyway? In its simplest form, faith is confidence or trust in a person or thing. To some people, faith has religious connotations. Dr. Fred Epstein is a world-famous pediatric neurosurgeon and director of the Institute for Neurology at Beth Israel Medical Center in New York. He has developed unprecedented techniques for the neurosurgical removal of brain-stem and spinal-cord tumors.

When Dr. Epstein agreed to become head of the hospital's new institute, he asked parents of some of his patients to assist them in designing a facility that would help the entire family get through a child's devastating illness. One of the suggestions from the parents was to have a weekly religious service which included the parents, the children, and the staff. "Religion is a great gift to a lot of people," says Epstein. "It doesn't matter what your religion is. The bottom line is, it's the same boss, different management. It's just that the faith that people have is enormously supportive to all of us here who have to deal with life-threatening problems every day."

Most of us don't have to deal with life-threatening problems every day. Our faith may be in simpler things, and is sometimes reinforced by the quietest moments in life. I am a big fan of Ralph Waldo Emerson, who once said, "All that I have seen teaches me to trust the Creator for all I have not seen." It is the beauty of the world, the miracle of life itself, that often inspires faith.

It is this quiet observance and reverence for the world that surrounds us that is true spirituality. How you choose to define your faith is a strictly personal decision. But most top achievers do believe in some power higher than themselves. Author James Redfield says he has come to the understanding that his best ideas come from a "source higher than me."

"It's a mystical experience, where one's higher ideas and even higher inspirations come from," he adds. "Whether it's a creative idea within an occupational or professional framework, or some sort of artistic endeavor. It seems these ideas come from a place higher than us. We really do have to be open to the mystical side of ourselves, the higher side of ourselves, in order to be fully open to our best potential and our most productive creativity."

The vast majority of the people I've interviewed about success talk about how faith—however they define it for themselves—has played an important role in their lives. When we look around and see the miracles that surround us—art and literature, beauty and grace, technology and science, and life itself—how can we doubt that there is something greater than ourselves? Adversity cannot get the better of us when faith is there to hold us up and keep us strong.

"I know this world is ruled by infinite intelligence. . . . Everything that surrounds us—everything that exists—proves that there are infinite laws behind it. There can be no denying this fact. It is mathematical in its precision."

—THOMAS A. EDISON

three

Organization

Don storms is a multimillionaire, one of the most successful Amway distributors in the country today. Several years ago, however, Don Storms was senior vice president of a highly successful nationally known televangelist organization. He loved his job. He was totally committed to his job, to the organization, and to the man for whom he worked. Then adversity struck. A new manager was hired whose vision for the organization did not agree with Storms's. Despite his years of service and dedication, Storms was fired.

He was devastated. "My first reaction was that I would just move to Alaska, get a little cabin, and fish. I didn't care about my family or anything else." This attitude did not last long. Very soon, Storms began to view his adversity as a blessing.

"Getting fired was the catalyst that drove me to work harder than

I ever had before. I was angry. I was out to prove to everyone that I could make something of my life."

That was the fuel that motivated Storms's success. "There is a fine line in adversity," Storms says. "If you cross over one side, you let that adversity eat you up inside. If you cross on the other side, adversity becomes the fuel that will fire your engine."

Storms used his adversity to fire his engine. With the help of a mentor named Dexter Yager, Storms began to steer himself toward a new horizon.

"I probably would never gotten into Amway if I hadn't been fired," says Storms. "I was on TV. I had a lot of fans. I'd have been there for life and been broke. But I believe God sometimes puts stop signs in front of us so that we will stop and turn in another direction."

What was it that allowed Don Storms to step over the right side of that line, to use adversity to fuel his engine, and to turn himself successfully in a new direction?

"It was a sense of purpose," he says. "Having a dream, a goal to strive toward." It was having this goal—making a success of his new business venture—that enabled Storms to keep going during the rough times.

"I'm a country boy," says Storms. "When we used to plow, we would never look right down at the ground we were plowing. We'd look at the oak tree, shoot for that, and plow a straighter furrow. If you look at the adversities—oh, there's a rock, or a tree stump, or a small ravine—you'll be wandering all over the place. But if you've got an oak tree in your sight and you're heading right for it, you'll get past the rocks and stumps and accomplish your goals."

"By concentrating our efforts upon a few major goals, our efficiency soars, our projects are completed—we are going somewhere. By focusing our efforts to a single point, we achieve the greatest result."
—FROM THE BEST OF SUCCESS, WYNN DAVIS

THE ENERGY OF GOALS

When we set goals that are important to us, they act as a magnet to keep us moving forward in a positive direction. Dreams do not come true by luck or magic; they become a reality by our setting small, achievable goals that are accomplished step by step, day by day.

We need goals to keep us going. It's easy to see this in our everyday lives. Think about those days (however few and far between they may be) when you don't have anything special to do. Maybe a few errands here and there, a phone call or two to make. You feel relaxed, even a bit lethargic. You watch TV, you fiddle around the house. Maybe the errands get done, maybe they don't. Such days can be great for giving us a break from our normal hurried routines, but they're not so good for getting things done.

Now think about days where specific tasks must be accomplished. With careful planning, they can all get done. You feel energized, and though you may be tired at the end of the day, you feel good for having "taken care of business."

We need goals to keep us energized and focused. I'm the type of person who likes (and needs) to have several different projects going at once. Occasionally, however, I start to get overwhelmed by all that I have to do. That's when I think about Don Storms's oak tree story. I refocus myself on the most important goal I need to work toward at that moment, and figure out what one step I can take right then to move myself forward.

In *Diamond in the Rough*, I introduced an acronym for the word "goals" that explains just how the process works:

- **G**ather as much information as you can on your goals, from as many sources as possible—books, audiotapes, people who have achieved similar goals before you.
- **O**rganize a step-by-step plan. Write down each step and how it can be accomplished.
- **A**ct on your plans. The most elaborate plan, never acted upon, is useless. Nothing gets done until you take an action.
- **L**ook back at the plan. Constantly reevaluate your goals (Is this the direction you want to take?), your plans (Is this the most logical step to take next?), and your actions (Is there anything else you can do today to reach your goal?).
- **S**et new goals. As soon as you reach one goal, set another, more challenging one.

As you can see, each letter of the acronym calls for an action step. If you follow each of these steps, you set up a natural energy flow that provides the "juice" you need to complete the next action step.

STRATEGIC THINKING

The Art of War is a book compiled over two thousand years ago by a man named Sun Tzu, a mysterious Chinese warrior and philosopher. *The Art of War* has been studied by soldiers and warlords in Asia for many centuries. In recent times, however, this book has also been studied by many of the world's most successful business leaders and entrepreneurs. This book's basic tenet, its most important principle, is "To win without fighting is best."

Sun Tzu believed that you could accomplish the most by doing the least. In other words, one needs to plan things out so carefully, and take such care of all the minor details, minutiae, and small steps as they arise, that in the end there is very little left to be done. This was Sun Tzu's advice to warriors of ancient times:

> *Plan for what is difficult while it is easy, do what is great while it is small. The most difficult things in the world must be done while they are still easy, the greatest things in the world done while they are still small. For this reason sages never do what is great, and this is why they can achieve greatness.*

The first chapter of *The Art of War* is devoted to the importance of strategy. According to Webster, strategy is defined as "a plan, method, or series of maneuvers . . . for obtaining a specific goal or result." We all know that not every battle is won by the strongest opponent. A small army with a better strategy can often outmaneuver even an army with more men, more equipment, and higher technology to support them.

Thus having a clear purpose, setting strong goals, and applying strategic thinking can help you defeat even the strongest "enemy" or adversity. *The Art of War* quotes Zhang Yu, a biographer of military leaders from the Sung Dynasty (960–1278):

When your strategy is deep and far-reaching, then what you gain by your calculations is much, so you can win before you even fight. When your strategic thinking is shallow and nearsighted, then what you gain by your calculations is little, so you lose before you do battle. Much strategy prevails over little strategy, so those with no strategy cannot but be defeated. Therefore it is said that victorious warriors win first and then go to war, while defeated warriors go to war first and then seek to win.

Of course, it's important to note that the very next chapter in *The Art of War* is called "Doing Battle." This means that you can't stay in your room planning and strategizing your life away and expect to accomplish anything. There comes a point when you must take action.

Tom Peters, best-selling author of *In Search of Excellence* and *The Pursuit of WOW,* once told me that one of his favorite quotes came from General George Patton, who said, "A good plan executed right now is highly preferable to a great plan executed next week."

"I'm all for planning and preparation, and learning and skill development," says Peters. "Anybody who denigrates that is a fool. On the other side of the coin—when opportunity knocks, go through the door at a hundred miles an hour. The fact that you haven't dotted all the i's and crossed all the t's is absolutely positively irrelevant. I think that's what has messed up a lot of American corporations. Twenty-five, thirty-five years ago, they got so enamored with their strategic plans, they forgot how to act."

PLAYING THROUGH THE PAIN

Although we'll talk a lot more about action in the next chapter, there is a point about it I want to make here. There are two kinds of action. One is scattershot, going in all directions. Certain things will be accomplished, but many more will be overlooked. The other kind of action is direct and focused, and requires long-term commitment. People are often fearful of making long-term commitments because they believe they're intractable. But any decision can be changed. And the more you're committed to a certain path, the more you learn about it. Knowledge eradicates fear. So the commitment becomes easier as you go on, even if you encounter rough spots in the beginning.

"It's like tennis and other racquet sports," says billionaire Morty Davis, Chairman of D. H. Blair Investment Banking Corp. "When you learn how to play tennis, at the beginning it hurts and bleeds. But if you stick with it, your hands become callused and it doesn't hurt.

"In life it's important to learn what the negatives are, because if you only have quick success, it is always doomed to failure. Ninety-eight percent of people who inherit or win large amounts of money, lose it; they don't know how to handle it. Worse than that, it takes away their drive. Even when they succeed, they feel like failures because they feel they bought their way in. Ultimately, it's good to have some tough times. That's what gives you calluses."

So what is it that keeps you going while the calluses are forming? Why don't we all just give up as soon as the pain appears? Some people do. But those who can focus more on the end result than on the temporary hardship can play through the pain and reach their goals.

Morty Davis had to play through a lot of pain to get to where he is today. He was born into abject poverty in Brooklyn, New York. He started working as a very young man, and worked at every kind of job imaginable, from backbreaking physical labor to rejection-laden door-to-door sales. What kept him going was that he always had specific goals in mind, things for which he had to keep striving. To Davis, it's having goals and striving toward them that makes his life exciting.

"It's the aspiration even more than the achievement," says Davis. "No reality is ever as good as the fantasy you have. When you do reach your goal, there is an inevitable letdown. It's the striving that makes life interesting and exciting."

It's Davis's point of view that life is actually very depressing. "We all start out as beautiful infants," he explains. "We're cute, we're vigorous, we're full of energy. If everything goes right for us, if we never have any accidents, if we never have any terrible diseases, if everything goes smoothly, we live to be eighty-seven and all wrinkled and arthritic and ultimately leave this world in a box. This is very depressing. The only way to avoid this depression is always to have some goal you're working toward that keeps you excited."

Success is always built on a strong sense of purpose, on the faith and belief and passion we have for the goals we set.

"If I offered you a job that could make you two or three million dollars a year, what would you say?" asks Davis. "Would you say, 'No, thanks, I love what I do'? The main element of success is to love what you do. Hopefully, it's something worthwhile. If you love to do drugs, that's not a worthwhile purpose. If you have a goal that's worthwhile, and it excites you, then that's success. . . . If I can't offer you enough money to change your job, that means you have ultimate success. Because people make money in order to do what they want to do. If that's what you're doing, then that's worth more than all the money in the world."

A SIMPLE SYSTEM OF ORGANIZATION

"Leaders are the most results-oriented people in the world, and this fixation with outcome is possible only if a person knows what he wants. Knowing what you want and being able to translate it into action are two of the most important keys to effective leadership."
—WARREN BENNIS, FROM *REINVENTING LEADERSHIP*

Setting goals is not really very difficult—once you know what you want. For many people, however, that seems to be a major stumbling block. The following is a simple system that will help you determine what goals are most important to you, and how to go about achieving those goals.

One important note: DO THIS EXERCISE RIGHT NOW.

All you need is a pen and a few pieces of paper. Go get them, come back, and start reading again. If you do this, you're on your way to developing the habit of taking rapid action on new ideas. In fact, any time you come across a useful idea in this book (or any other), take action on it immediately. Because if you delay even twenty-four hours, the likelihood is that you'll never do it at all. Worse than that, you'll develop the habit of *not* taking action on good ideas.

That said, here is the most powerful goal-setting technique I've ever used. I've seen more results from this technique for myself and for others I know, than from any other system out there. The two things that make this the most powerful system are (1) it's easy to do, and (2) it commits you to take action.

1. Take a piece of paper and write down ten goals for the next twelve months. You may want to lose some weight, increase your income, get a better car, change jobs, change relationships, take a trip. It doesn't matter what it is, just write down ten things.

The very act of writing these things down will change you. You will now move into the top 3 percent of Americans. Because only 3 percent of Americans have actually written down their goals. If you do nothing more than write down your goals, and if you look at this list one year later, you'll be staggered to find that at least eight of those goals have been achieved to some extent. You might even have forgotten the goals you wrote down, and yet you will find you've made substantial progress on most of them.

2. To go to the next level, choose the most important goal on the list. To do that, ask yourself, "Which one of these goals, if I were to achieve it, would have the greatest positive impact on my life?" Pick one goal that meets that criterion, and write it on top of a piece of paper.

Suppose the goal is to increase your income to $50,000 a year.

Write it out as a question: "How can I increase my income to $50,000 over the next twelve months?" Make the question as specific as possible. The more specific the question, the more specific the answers it will draw out of your subconscious mind.

3. Write down twenty answers to the question. Force yourself to list twenty answers. The first three, four, or five answers will be easy. The next five will be hard. The last ten will be extraordinarily difficult. At the end of the exercise, you'll probably be exhausted—but you must do one more thing. Choose one of the items on your list of twenty answers. Pick the thing that is most obvious, that grabs you first, and *do it*. NOW. Immediately. Pick up the phone. Write that letter. Move. Buy. Cross the street—whatever that action is, do it without hesitation.

These three steps, the whole process, up to the point of taking the action, should take you about fifteen to twenty minutes. However, if you do this exercise, one year from now your life will be different. You will be accomplishing more. You'll be happier. You'll feel more powerful and in control. You'll be making more money, making strides in your career, building better relationships—whatever it is you set out to do.

This exercise is a true test of who you are. It doesn't cost you anything. All you have to do is write down ten goals, pick the one that will have the most positive impact on your life, write down twenty ways to achieve that goal, and take one immediate action step. If you can do that, the world is yours.

A REALITY CHECK

There is one important factor to keep in mind when you're setting goals. You must do a reality check on your plans and dreams. Is what you want achievable in the real world? There may be some compromises that have to be made concerning your dreams, or some reformatting, so that the dreams conform with what is actually possible.

For instance, you can't realistically say, "I want to fly, so I'm going to grow wings and soar." However, if you really want to fly, you can probably find a way. You can do research on all the flying mechanisms that have been invented so far. You may find something, like hang gliding, that satisfies your yearn to be airborne, or you may end up inventing something yourself.

Everything is achievable if you're willing to put in the effort, and to make certain compromises and sacrifices. You may have to give your dream more time than you initially planned, or make it happen on a smaller scale. The hours you put in, the research you do, the setbacks you experience—those are reality. You will hit a lot of obstacles, you will experience failure. But the failures you have will bring you closer to success.

That is what happens to scientists and inventors all the time. No invention ever came along a straight path from idea to reality. It may take hundreds, or even thousands, of tries before an idea gets from someone's fertile imagination to being a real-life working model. Trial and error are the greatest teachers of all. When you find out what doesn't work, when you find out that the pathway you have chosen has insurmountable obstacles, it's time to say, "Okay, it won't work this way, I'll have to try another method." If you don't give up, you'll find the way that does work.

You can't just wish you had millions of dollars and play the lottery, or dream of being a movie star and never get up off the couch. When you go out and do the research and put in the effort, then your plan becomes reality-based. Whenever you start a project, there will be some people who say, "That's not realistic." For them, perhaps it's not. But they don't know you, and what you have to bring to the plan or project.

But even research and effort cannot perform miracles. Suppose someone who is tone-deaf and has no sense of rhythm wants to be a famous opera singer. That person could study with the best singers and teachers in the world for the rest of his or her life, a lack of talent and aptitude would still be that individual's reality. It is inevitable that he or she will fail at this. Success is finding a goal, moving toward it, and consistently setting newer, higher goals. Therefore, failure is inevitable if you set unrealistic goals. If you do set unrealistic goals, you will be frustrated all the time and unable to move forward.

I'm a big believer in setting goals. I set goals for every aspect of my life. Not only do I write them down, I write them on giant chalkboards and hang them on the walls of my office so that I can remind myself, when need be, of the things on which I should be focusing. Occasionally, I set goals I cannot reach. When I look back and evaluate, I realize there were reasons for these "failures." (I don't really look at them as failures, because valuable lessons have been learned from them.)

The reason those goals were not reached was that they were too big. They could not be achieved in one giant leap, and I did not take all the little steps it would have taken to reach the desired destination. For that is how any goal is reached—step by tiny step. It's like a spiderweb. A spider spins a web strand by strand until it is all connected and strong enough to catch a fly. Like the spider, you are building your foundation strand by strand, making connections, until it is strong enough to "catch" your goal.

Take a teacher, for instance, who has a broad subject to cover over the semester. He or she can't teach the whole subject in one class. Nor can that teacher just walk into class each day and "wing it." In order to be sure of reaching the goal by the end of the year, that teacher has to make lesson plans that break the broad subject down into monthly, weekly, and daily teaching units. It's the only way he or she can reach the goal.

That teacher is creating *reality-based action*. This is what we all must do to reach our goals.

Too many times goal setting consists of "I want to be the number-one sales rep," or "I want to travel around the world," or "I want to make a million dollars in two years." There's nothing intrinsically wrong with these goals. But if you try to accomplish any one of them, you'll find the task too big. You need to break the goal down into manageable daily actions: what you need to do every day, every week, every month. That's the tough part. It calls for patience, persistence, and follow-through. But every time even the smallest goal is accomplished, it gives you the confidence boost you need to keep moving on to the next step.

There are always going to be those days when we don't feel quite as energized, when all we want to do is be lazy. Those are the days that, more than others, you need to take action—to make the decision to get out there, to pick up the phone, to write that letter, to make that appointment, to try something new. Do as much as you can while you have the time. As time goes by, there are always more and more distractions. By doing all the little things as soon as they come up, you're building that strong foundation you need.

WRITING OUT A BUSINESS PLAN FOR LIFE

When I talked with Morty Davis about organization and goal setting, he told me that the first thing he asks of a company in which D. H. Blair is considering investing is that they submit a business plan. This business plan clearly lays out the goal of the company, the ideas behind the goal, and the steps necessary to reach that goal. He gives each prospective company a business plan outline to follow. I have adapted this outline for people who want to design their own future. Here is the plan.

Business Plan for Life

Executive Summary
- General overview/description of plan or goal
- What is the overall strategy for achieving that goal?
- What makes you uniquely qualified to pursue this goal?

Background
- How did the idea come about?
- When did you start working on this idea?
- What has happened since its inception?

Product
- What is the product (or the desired end result)?
- How does the product, service, or idea work?
- What is the value proposition (what benefits does it offer users)?

Marketing
- Who is the customer/beneficiary of this product or service?
- What are people doing today in the absence of the product, service, or idea?
- How will the product, service, or idea be priced?
- How will it be promoted or distributed?

Competition
- Who or what is in competition with your product, service, or idea?
- If competition is not relevant, are you trying to raise your own standards? From what to what?

Organization
- When this goal is reached, can it be managed and maintained by you alone?
- If not, who can help you manage and maintain the goal?
- What experience do you (and your potential partners) have in managing your particular goal?

Financial
- How much capital is needed?
- What specifically will the money be used for?
- How much money has been invested in the project so far?
- Can you realistically project profits (financial and otherwise) of attaining this goal?

Following this plan will bring any goal into reality-based action. It will also clarify your thinking, so that if it is necessary to explain your ideas to someone else, you will be able to present them logically and concisely.

Every goal needs a plan. Fail to plan, plan to fail. Goals can only be achieved by understanding and acting upon each small, important step that gives the goal its foundation. It takes time and effort to reach a goal, and most people are not willing to invest in either of those things unless the reward is immense and immediate.

You don't have to follow the plan exactly. Even if you answer only a few of the questions, you will be able to determine whether or not your goal is realistic. And your answers may change as you begin to put your plan into action. You may realize that the small steps you're taking are not really moving you toward your goal; the steps are not appropriate, or the goal is too high. Adversity may rear its ugly head just when you are nearing your goal, and force you to make compromises you would not have made before. Goals are not written in stone. Adjustments can always be made.

But having these goals can also help to get you through the adversity. When you are feeling lost, confused, or overwhelmed, your goals can help you clear your mind and regain a sense of purpose and direction.

"The world has the habit of making room for the person whose words and actions show that he knows where he is going."
—NAPOLEON HILL

PERSPECTIVE, REEVALUATION, AND KNOWING WHO YOU ARE

"Leaders allow themselves to develop many opportunities for nurturing their strengths through goal setting. They're like good athletes—they challenge themselves constantly. They also surround themselves with different ways of getting feedback on how they're doing. I think most good athletes, like most good leaders, need feedback to evaluate how far they are from their goals."
—WARREN BENNIS, FROM *REINVENTING LEADERSHIP*

When we experience success, we are usually quick to give ourselves credit for it. We say, "I did this, and I did that, and that's why this plan succeeded." When we fail, we are quick to blame everyone and everything else. We say, "This person did that, and these circumstances were terrible, and that's why this plan failed." We look inside when we have success and outside when we fail. What we really need to do is look for both outside and inside causes for failure and success.

Every once in a while, it is important to take a look at what you're doing, think about why you're doing it, and make sure you're on the right track. This happened to me several years ago when I was working on a special project that was going to take a famous comedian and syndicate him on radio. This project wasn't the main core of my business, but sometimes you need to take your foot off first in order to get to second. Anything of greatness in the world requires some form of risk and sacrifice, as we've discussed. I've achieved many successes, but I've also experienced a lot of rejection and setbacks. But to this day I wouldn't trade any of the hard times, because of the lessons that have been learned.

With this project, I had worked thousands of hours and spent a considerable amount of money. We had radio stations lined up and advertisers committed. But because of contractual disagreements, we did not move ahead. I believe in the win-win. When a project is not set up to be profitable, with incentives, for both sides, we must learn how to walk away and move on.

One morning after the project had fallen through, I woke up and my wife looked and me and said, "Honey, a great deal of funds have just flown out the window." My wife is the most supportive person in my life. She's never negative and always takes the positive view of things. This was the first time I had ever seen her concerned about our financial situation. Like most other people, we have a mortgage, kids, and overhead. When you're focused on a dream and money is going out the window, it often takes something like her statement to jolt you out of it. This was probably the greatest wake-up call I ever had.

For the next month I worked like a maniac, sometimes until 3 or 4 A.M. I ended up generating about eight months of business in less than thirty days. Sometimes adversity has a way of helping us see much clearer, work much harder. Some would call the project with the famous comedian a failure. No way. It helped me start my own radio show out of New York City. I made tremendous advertising contacts and learned a great deal about radio syndication. I also made major connections, with people like Evander Holyfield, Barbara Mandrell, Bruce Jenner, Don Rickles, and many other high achievers who came on the show and shared their ideas.

I've used all I learned from the project to help me move forward into the future, and the temporary financial setback, with my wife's help, galvanized me to work even harder. Failure isn't failure as long as we learn the valuable lessons it teaches us and apply them the next time. So the next time something goes wrong, or something does not go as planned, stop looking to put blame on other people for the lack of accomplishment. Look for what you can learn from that setback, and then immediately apply it to a new venture.

Another person who heads straight toward his goals and learns from his setbacks is Perry Wolff, an Emmy award–winning screenwriter, producer, and director whose documentary short subject *An Essay on Matisse* was nominated for a 1996 Academy Award.

"The most important thing in life is to have a goal," says Wolff. "The cliché thing to say is to get there by knowing who you are. But I always say you have to start by knowing who you are not. Deciding what you're not is the beginning. Little children want to be everything. They want to be a fireman, an astronaut, a rock and roll star, and president of the United States. Eventually they sort things out by realizing which of those things they don't want to be.

"Early on in my career, I decided that I wanted to be involved in nonfiction in radio, television, and movies. I was sorely tempted to be what I was not, to go after the offers of 'adventures in Hollywood.' But that's not me. That isn't what I wanted to do."

Pursuing what he wanted to do wasn't always easy. Wolff was fired from several jobs. But he thinks it's a good thing to get fired. Wolff tells the story of a friend of his named Teddy White, who was working for Henry Luce, the head of Time-Life. White wrote a novel about the experience of being fired, called *The View from the Fortieth Floor.*

"I don't remember much about the novel," says Wolff, "but I do remember the last line. It was 'He looked back and it was just another building in Manhattan.' That's what you have to do sometimes. Put things in perspective. You're going to get hit by adversity and it's going to be painful. In some cases you never get over the hurt. But in most cases, you have to come to the conclusion that 'it's just another building in Manhattan.' "

Only you know what you are truly able to do. You can't let the person who fires you, or rejects your work, or puts you down, determine your future success. Picasso eventually became the richest artist of the twentieth century. But for a time, he was the poorest. He was being paid $1 a day for his output. A dealer was able to sell some of his early paintings, but when Picasso started painting everything in shades of blue (which became known as his Blue Period), the dealer said, "I can't sell these. I'm going to have to drop you as a client." Picasso didn't listen. And he went into a period of abysmal poverty. But just a few years ago, a Japanese art collector bought one of his Blue Period paintings for over $59 million.

★   ★   ★

Success is attained by setting goals and following through. By having foresight and faith—by envisioning our goals and believing that they can be reached—we can do anything we set our minds to. When you're afraid to set important goals because they appear distant and unreachable, don't think of yourself as starting at Point A and magically arriving at Point B. Instead, envision yourself going through each step, learning from your mistakes, and, most of all, *enjoying yourself and your great adventure.*

four

Concentrated Effort and Courage

SLOW AND STEADY WINS THE RACE

"Nothing in the world can take the place of persistence. Talent will not; nothing is more common than unsuccessful men with talent. Genius will not; unrewarded genius is almost a proverb. Education will not; the world is full of educated derelicts. Persistence and determination alone are omnipotent."

—CALVIN COOLIDGE

THINGS ARE RARELY accomplished by one great burst of energy; success comes through continuing on day after day, long past the time when you think you *should* be successful. Those who persist, who continue steadily in their course of action, in spite of opposition and obstacles, will win in the end.

Persistence is well known in the animal kingdom. David Attenborough, in his book *The Trials of Life: A Natural History of Animal Behavior*, tells about the kusimanse, a dwarf mongoose from West Africa. The kusimanse lives on chicken's eggs. When it finds an egg it "puts its forelegs over it and with a vigor that would not disgrace an American footballer, hurls it backwards through its splayed hind legs." The animal does this over and over again until the egg cracks.

Then there's the Egyptian vulture, which lives on ostrich eggs. When the vulture finds a nest of eggs, it picks up large stones in its beak and "with a nod of its head, tosses them in the general direction of the nest. What it lacks in aim, it makes up for in persistence until it manages to break open one of the eggs."

Among the many traits that successful people have in common, persistence is one of the strongest. They don't give up. If need be, they throw their stones over and over again. When they face rejection, they get angry, use that anger to say, "I'll show you!" and they keep on going. When they meet obstacles, they find ways around them. When they get tired, they don't quit; they find something to rejuvenate themselves and they start again.

Persistence has two elements: Number one is having a goal, and number two is moving toward it. Once the goal is in your heart, and you dream about it and you live it and you believe in it, you will do anything it takes to get there.

Sometimes we can succeed by persistence alone. Perhaps you are trying to reach someone who is never available, and won't return your messages. You can give up and try someone else. Or you can keep calling. Many times, you will simply wear the other person down, until finally he says, "This guy is still calling? Let me take the call this time." Usually, though, there is a faster way to get through, and that is by offering value along with your persistence.

Be sure you have a reason to keep calling. Every step you take must be of value, to yourself and to other people. Ninety-nine percent of the time, reaching your goal means interaction with other people. You may need help from them in order to accomplish your task. Try to understand what their goals are, as well as your own. Get them on your side. Learn what's important to them, and what you can bring to the table to help them. It's not just increasing the quantity of your actions that counts, it's making every action more efficient.

Persistence also means constant improvement. If you keep doing the same thing over and over again, in just the same way, you'll always get the same results. So as you keep going, you must learn from every step you take. When that happens as you continue your efforts, you'll find shortcuts that increase your efficiency and make each action more meaningful than the last.

THE ANCIENT ART OF CONCENTRATED EFFORT

"Man may remove all obstacles through quiet perseverance."

—CHINESE PROVERB

81

Making each action meaningful is the essence of concentrated effort. I first came across this phrase when I was reading about the ancient Chinese martial art of Kung Fu. In their book *Kung Fu: History, Philosophy and Technique*, David Chow and Richard Spangler define Kung Fu as "the mastery of an art, an accomplishment or difficult task through highly concentrated effort. It ultimately means a lot of hard work or practice. Kung = accomplishment, Fu = effort. In Western terms it can be said that Muhammad Ali achieved Kung Fu in boxing; Michelangelo attained Kung Fu in art; Ernest Hemingway reached Kung Fu in literature."

There are many relevant concepts in Kung Fu, similar to those found in *The Art of War* from the last chapter. A person does not become a master of Kung Fu to fight and destroy. The purpose of this ancient art is to serve and protect while avoiding conflict if at all possible. The art of Kung Fu is not to be taken lightly. To become a master in any of the Kung Fu methods (there are many), one must practice for many years. Some of the methods may seem impossible to master; in fact, there is no one in modern history who has been able to perform some of the tasks. One such method is called Red Sand Palm, where a master merely makes a sign of rubbing or striking an opponent with the palm of his hand from a distance, and the opponent will be fatally wounded.

Another method is called Hing Kung, which is the art of walking on any substance, including sand, grass, and snow, without leaving footprints. This requires years of intensive practice, first balancing on the edge of big-bellied earthenware jars filled with rocks, then balancing with the rocks removed. Practitioners then walk on reed baskets, then on sand covered with rice paper, then finally on sand leaving no footprints. Kung Fu masters agree that it takes over ten years to perfect this art.

There is only one way to become a master of Hing Kung, and that is by concentrated effort, day in and day out. You cannot proceed to the next step of practice until the last one has been mastered. It takes tremendous discipline, and tremendous patience. The Hing Kung student does not allow anything to distract him from his goal. He knows that he will fall off the rim of the jar, crush the reed basket, and rip the rice paper thousands of times before he can achieve "light walking." Yet every time he falls, he gets up and begins again.

You don't have to become a master of Hing Kung to utilize the principles of Kung Fu and concentrated effort. You can become a master of whatever you pursue by adding discipline and patience, by practicing your craft over and over, no matter how many times you fall or fail, and by believing that in the end you will be successful.

This philosophy is embodied in the life and work of Tony Wainright, an advertising director, director of six public companies, writer of books, movies, and plays, and a consultant to Fortune 500 companies across the country. When I interviewed Tony for this book, it was 6 A.M. his time. He had a torn cartilage in his knee which he had not yet had time to correct, his father was dying in a hospital in the Midwest, and he had popped a blood vessel in his right eye the night before.

"I only tell you these things," he said, "because, as anyone who knows me will tell you, I won't let these things stop me. There is nothing that can stop me."

When Wainright was a young boy of six, he was small for his age. So his parents sent him to martial arts school (which was unheard of in those days).

"Martial arts taught me concentration," he says. "It taught me to overcome pain and adversity. It taught me that I could do things I never thought possible. It taught me resilience, and it changed my entire life."

It also taught him about patience and persistence. Once, there was a company he wanted as an advertising account. The first time he went to see them, they told him the timing was wrong. Wainright pursued this company for six years. Lots of people told him to give up. But each time he called on the company, they gave him the same answer. "The timing is wrong." Then one day, in the sixth year, the company told him, "We're starting a new division. How would you like the account?" He walked out of their offices that day with $30 million worth of their business.

"I kept going back because I have the utmost confidence in my skills," says Wainright. "I know I can deliver, and I knew I would get something out of my persistence. I can't say it works every single time, but I'm successful more times than not. The analogy I would use is, if you stand by a door, the odds are at some juncture the door will open. If you find the door closed and you walk away saying, 'Gee, the door is closed and I can't get in,' you'll never get in the door. I'm willing to stand by the door."

Wainright wasn't always so confident, and he wasn't always so successful. When he was twenty-nine years old, three hardships hit him at once. First, he became seriously ill with ileitis, which called for major surgery. Shortly after that, he lost his job. He had one child, another one on the way, and very little income. Then the most serious adversity struck: His second daughter was born with spina bifida and she died within a year.

"I got down on my knees and I remember thinking, There are only two ways to go," says Wainright. "I'm either going to pull myself together, or I'm not. I pulled myself together. The good news is that from that adversity two things happened. First, I worked harder than ever before and became successful. Second, which is more important, I never forgot what happened to me. I turned my life around and, from that moment on, dedicated a portion of it to helping other people, doing things I never would have thought of had I not gone through adversity myself.

"I've had lots of adversity in my life. For me, there are three components that helped me get through it. One is prayer. It's private, and it's important. Another is the absolute belief that tomorrow will be better than today. And the third, though it may sound like a cliché, is that I don't take things personally. If something happens to me, instead of belaboring it and worrying about it, I figure out a way to overcome it, or else I'll move on and come back to it later. That's probably the most salient advice I can give to anyone. Don't dwell on things. And don't give up. Don't feel sorry for yourself when something happens. It happens to everyone, and it happens more than once. The ultimate winners are the ones that never give up."

★　　★　　★

Nobody knows about persistence and never giving up more than an inventor. Inventions do not go from the mind to drawing board to the marketplace in a straight line. There is always an incredible number of failures that come before the finished product. There is an enormous amount of work between the original idea and the point at which people are actually using the invention. Every single step along the way presents unique problems that have to be solved before the process can continue.

Art Fry was working for the 3M Company when he had an idea for a temporary adhesive—something you could use as a bookmark, for example, that wouldn't fall out but that wouldn't ruin the pages, either.

"With any invention," says Fry, "it's like a jigsaw puzzle. There are all sorts of parts that have to fit together. They're not always obvious when you start the journey, but they've all got to be done. You've got manufacturing problems, and marketing problems. You've got government regulations. You've got to get a good patent that protects you. There's an enormous amount of work, but it's all doable. You've just got to keep at it, and if you fail, try something else.

"Don't give up. It's a statistical thing. For every success, there are hundreds of failures. I've had many people come up to me and say, 'You know, I had the idea for a self-attaching note, too.' I believe them, because when many people are confronted with the same problem, many people will think of a solution. But there are far fewer who will go ahead and do something about it—do all the work required to take that idea and solve all the problems connected with it and build it into a business. Not many people are willing to put in that much work."

It is only those people who are willing to put in the work who can withstand the inevitable adversity that accompanies any worthwhile pursuit. It is only those people who understand that adversity *is* inevitable who can keep their faith and belief strong while the struggle is ongoing. Brian Tracy, motivational speaker and author of *Maximum Achievement and Advanced Selling Strategies*, told me of a principle of success he learned many years ago.

"The time to develop your character is in advance of adversity," says Tracy. "You don't wait until there's an accident to take a first aid course. You take it in advance so that you are prepared. The key to success is to say, 'I am going to pursue this goal and I'm going to encounter a lot of setbacks and obstacles. But I am not going to quit. No matter what happens, it's not going to stop me. It may slow me down, it may disappoint me, but it's not going to stop me.'

"You must prepare yourself mentally. Because when you get hit in the emotional solar plexus, your first reaction will be to feel psychologically stunned. You will feel like quitting. You'll feel like you shouldn't have done it in the first place. You'll get down on yourself. But if you're prepared, your second reaction will be to bounce back."

Once adversity strikes, it's too late to prepare yourself mentally. That's why many people fall apart. They don't expect to fail, and when they do, they have no psychological reserves. And when they quit, they set up a habit of quitting. The most successful people develop a habit of persistence. Successful people think about quitting, too—they just don't do it.

It takes an incredible intensity of effort to keep from quitting when the pressure is on. Sometimes it takes everything you have to keep on going. Just ask Heavyweight Champion Evander Holyfield about the lesson he learned from his first fight with boxer Riddick Bowe, whom Holyfield considers his toughest opponent.

"That fight was a struggle and it went back and forth," says Holyfield. "I was competing against a young man who was as talented as I was and just as strong as I was and who had just as much knowledge of the game as I did. But I was determined to finish, to really see what the end would be. While I was fighting, I couldn't tell how well I was doing, but I knew that I would never know the outcome if I quit. I was able to finish, even though he got the decision. But when I got an opportunity to see the tape, I felt much better because I saw that at one point I really could have quit. I was so happy that I didn't, I thanked God that I was able to finish, and that inspired me to come back and fight him again—and beat him."

THE MODERN ART OF ACTION

The art of concentrated effort is not the only lesson we learn from history. We also learn that there comes a time when we must take all the discipline, all the practice, all the patiently applied planning, and go into action. As a role model for this, we can look all the way back to Alexander the Great. It took Alexander ten years—from the time he was twenty-three to his death at the age of thirty-three—to conquer most of the known world. Alexander has been studied and admired throughout the centuries for his incredible willingness and ability to take action in the face of adversity.

This is made even more interesting by the fact that Alexander's armies were always outnumbered, sometimes by as much as twenty to one. But Alexander's philosophy was to attack so swiftly and move so quickly that his soldiers didn't have time to be afraid. He knew that fear is the greatest obstacle to success. The more we think about all the possible reasons something won't work out, the more our fear paralyzes us, and we end up not taking any action at all. The most successful people think about what it is they want or need to do, make decisions, make plans—and then act quickly. They move ahead of their fears. They literally outrun the fear, so that fear doesn't have a chance to catch them and slow them down.

Brian Tracy, a great admirer of Alexander the Great, reminded me of a quotation he had heard: "On the beaches of hesitation lie the bleached bones of those, who, at the moment of victory, hesitated, and in hesitating, lost all."

"This is a meaningful quotation," says Tracy, "because it's amazing how many people will pursue their goals until they're 95 percent there, and give up. Look at salespeople, for instance. They work terribly hard to make a sale. They get the sale, and then, at the moment of crucial importance, they give up, when all the research shows that this is the time you've got to redouble your efforts to make sure the sale stays together."

"All great masters are chiefly distinguished by the power of adding a second, a third, and perhaps a fourth step in a continuous line. Many a man has taken the first step. With every additional step you enhance immensely the value of your first."

—RALPH WALDO EMERSON

The American Management Association recently conducted a study of engineers in high-tech companies. They looked at those who were on the fast track in getting promoted and those who weren't, trying to find the critical difference between them. They looked at such factors as age, education, experience, networking, attendance at seminars, and personal development. The study found that one significant factor was action orientation, which was defined as the willingness to take initiative above and beyond what the person would normally be expected to do in his or her job.

When the AMA asked the engineers if they were action-oriented, they all answered yes. But when the ones who were not on the fast track were asked to explain what that meant, they said, "When the phone rings, I answer it," or "When I get an assignment, I do it," or "When there's a meeting, I go to it." The fast-trackers, on the other hand, said that they picked up the phone and called people, they sought out assignments, and they looked for, or even organized, meetings to increase their personal development and skill levels. They took the initiative, and they took risks.

Brian Tracy has also studied what makes some people successful and others not, and has recently written a book about what he calls the "luck factor." His conclusion? That luck does not really exist.

"People create their own luck," says Tracy. "Luck is really a matter of enhanced possibilities that bring about a result far faster than would normally be expected. In other words, a lucky person increases the likelihood that he or she will be lucky. A salesperson who calls on ten people is going to be luckier in terms of finding a viable prospect than a salesperson who calls on two people. An actor who tries out for twenty parts is going to be far luckier than an actor who goes to only two auditions. A student who does more assignments and turns them in on time is going to be much luckier in getting good grades, getting scholarships, and getting job recommendations. So we create our own luck by increasing the frequency of the activities that are most likely to lead us to the success that we desire."

Tracy adds one more important point concerning luck and action orientation: The unsuccessful person looks only to himself, and thinks only, What do I want to do? The successful person looks around him and says, What does the environment require? What do my customers require? What do the people I want to influence require? Successful people start by looking outside of themselves. Then they come back to themselves and say, "Based on what the environment requires of me, what am I most uniquely capable of providing to that environment?"

We are given only one life, and we are given each day only once. The saddest people on earth are those who live in regret for not taking advantage of the gifts and opportunities they had been given. And most regret is not about actions that were taken and that we wish we had not done; most regret is about the things we did not do.

"This is the beginning of a brand new day. God has given us this day to use as we desire. Now we can waste it or use it for good. But what we do today is important because we are exchanging this day of our lives for it. When tomorrow comes, this day will be gone forever, leaving in its place something we have traded for it. We want it to be gain, not loss. We want it to be good, not evil. We want it to be success, not failure, in order that we shall not regret the price we paid for it."

—ANCIENT PARABLE

THE TIMELESS ART OF WORKING HARD

Some of the most "uniquely capable" people in history have been artists. True artists express their imagination and vision in ways that belong only to them. The best artists of course have enormous talent, but what they have most in common is their ability and willingness to do the work.

In documentary-maker Perry Wolff's *Essay on Matisse,* the great artist is asked to what he attributes his great success. Matisse answers, "Hard work."

Matisse knew the meaning of hard work. He painted and re-painted his canvasses many times. He once said, "A masterpiece is never finished, it is just abandoned." Matisse's father wanted him to be a grain merchant and a lawyer. But at the age of twenty-one, Matisse became gravely ill. To help him pass the time, his mother gave him some paper and crayons. From that time on, all he wanted to do was paint.

Matisse studied painting with the masters of his time. He could have made a good living from the government, painting church ceilings in the style of the masters, which he did for a time. Then he found he just couldn't do that anymore; he had to follow his own style. So, even though he had a wife and three children to support, he refused the government subsidy and worked day and night on his own paintings.

Another example is Michelangelo. He began as an artist's appren-tice, chipping stones from a quarry. Before he ever sculpted one piece, he spent months chipping away at these stones. And it taught him well. He learned to really see the veins in the stones, to know how the rock would break. Because of that knowledge, he was able to create masterpieces in stone, such as his statue of David.

When Michelangelo painted the Sistine Chapel, he did almost all of it by himself. And he had to invent the process as he went along.

"To paint a fresco," Perry Wolff explains, "you have to have wet paint and wet plaster, and you have a limited time frame in which to work. You have two hours to put down the plaster, two hours to paint, and two hours to guess what will happen to your color as it dries. In those days, you didn't get color out of a tube, you had to mix your own. So there he was, painting and plastering and inventing sixty-two feet above the floor of the chapel. Most people think he painted lying on his back. He didn't. He painted reaching up to the ceiling, with the paint and the plaster constantly falling in his face."

The world would be a much poorer place if it wasn't for the persistence and hard work of artists like these. Their art truly lies in the painting and repainting of the canvas, in the chipping away of the stones at the quarry. These artists did not settle for the easy paths in life. To them, each brush stroke, each pounding of the hammer and chisel was the true challenge. In life, it is each little step that contains the seed of great art. Life is in the journey, not the destination. As we go through our daily challenges, that is where the greatness lies. That is where the learning lies; that is where the excitement lies. When the destination is reached, it's time to move on to the next challenge.

Josh Weston is the chairman of ADP, a company with $4 billion in revenues and thirty-three thousand employees. He believes that you have to "work success." That means that you have to keep trying, over and over again. He believes that a lot of companies, and a lot of people, fail because they are afraid to meet the next challenge and give up too soon. "The first time you try anything, whether it's a sale, a new product, or a new idea, it's not going to work that well," says Weston. "All too often in our society, people are inclined to try something once, and if it doesn't work, forget about it. As opposed to trying something once and being ready and willing to fix it, nine, ten, twelve more times until in the end you get it to work. Working success doesn't come just by swinging the bat once. It's persistence that makes for success."

Weston encourages his employees to keep going all the time, and to keep going for higher stakes. He often uses a pole-vaulting analogy to teach people about going one step further. In pole-vaulting, no matter how high you jump, even if nobody else in the world ever jumped that high, they don't automatically give you a gold medal. They raise the bar another inch and say "Try for more." It's important to keep the pole-vaulting analogy in mind during those times when we want to sit back and take it easy, simply because we may have made some small gains, or taken a step toward our goals. That is just the time to raise the bar again.

ALL WORK AND NO PLAY . . .

Josh Weston also has a warning for our society: Beware of putting too much emphasis on hard work. That would seem to contradict everything this chapter is about. But it doesn't. What he is talking about is what he calls "ADP math." The formula is: Thirty-nine plus one equals more than forty plus zero.

"Here's what I mean," says Weston. "A forty plus zero person is someone with an in basket full of paper, the phone is ringing all the time, head down, handling it all. Zero time to think about What am I doing, how am I doing it, why am I doing it, should I do it all, how do I do it better?

"Thirty-nine plus people have the same darn in basket, phone ringing every thirty seconds—but they take one of those forty hours to ask themselves those questions and find the answers. And they get twice as much done in those thirty-nine hours than the forty plus zero person ever will."

It's not only time to think that's important. For Jim McCann, founder and nationally known spokesman of 1-800-FLOWERS, who started out as a social worker and ended up running a $300 million company, the definition of success is "to have a high fun ratio in your life. We can't have 100 percent fun in everything we do, but for me, my fun index is 95 percent. That means 95 percent of the things I spend my days and weeks on are fun. I enjoy my work and I have fun at it. And that enables me to do the 5 percent of things that aren't fun."

Another important element, besides fun, is having some quiet time in our lives. Taking the time to think about the values in life, the things that are most important to us. We can't think about work all the time. We have family, friends, and our mental health to think about. Sometimes, when we get caught up in the hustle of everyday life, and we are so intent on reaching our goals, it's easy to forget what's best for our souls.

Not long ago I spent a vacation with my family in a rustic cabin overlooking a pond. I took my three-year-old son out in a canoe for the first time. It was dead quiet. We could feel a gentle breeze and hear the slight tinkling of the water beneath us. There were no distractions other than the sounds of nature. The pure quality of this time spent with my son led me to write this poem to express my feelings:

Through silence and comfort I can see clearly what nature provides.
I can feel the water as we cut fresh lines on glass.

I can see the wonder in my son's eyes as a new sensation surrounds
his curiosity.
How the simple and serene can say so much.
It is the quiet time away that reveals the true beauty of the child.

When I came back from this quiet time away, I was renewed and refreshed. I was able to go back to work with a clear sense of direction and focus. I had a renewed sense of confidence that I would be able to deal with whatever might present itself.

THE HEART OF THE MATTER

That deep core-based sense of confidence is not something that we are necessarily born with. It comes from having tried and failed, and risen to try again. It comes from experience, from having confronted one's fears and lived to tell the tale. It comes from the courage that is born in our hearts.

The word "courage" comes from the Latin *cuer*, or heart. It means the quality of mind or spirit that enables one to face danger, pain, or difficulty, instead of withdrawing from it. Courage does not mean the absence of fear. Those who are without fear are reckless and thoughtless, and often cause harm to themselves and others. Those who have courage know fear, yet carry on despite it. They are able to look fear in the face, acknowledge it, and say, "I will not let you stop me."

The problem with courage is one of perception. Most of us think that courage only applies to the big things: to saving someone's life, or to bravery in extreme circumstances. But everyone in this book, and in life, who has struggled day to day to overcome adversities large and small has shown great amounts of courage when he or she has pressed on with concentrated effort instead of just giving up. It's the opposite of being discouraged. It's looking inside yourself, being honest with yourself, knowing that going after your dreams may be difficult and you may not succeed, but, in the end, choosing to follow your heart because you know it is right and good. That is courage.

There are many quotes by Mark Twain that I love, but there is one that made an indelible mark on my memory. He said, "Through ignorance and confidence, success is sure." Many people are afraid to follow their dreams because they think they are not smart enough, or don't have enough information, or can't achieve anything because they're not "experts" in a particular field. But that theory just doesn't hold water. Take the Hale-Bopp comet, for instance. It was discovered by two different people simultaneously—one was an expert astronomer with years of professional experience, and the other was an amateur with a telescope set up in his backyard. Both got their names on the comet.

In business, it's often people who are not experts that attain the most success. I've spent a lot of my life in sales, and I've seen one phenomenon over and over again. A rookie salesperson will come in with no experience whatsoever; the next thing you know he or she is salesperson of the year. Many times it's because of the salesperson's ignorance of what it supposedly takes to be successful. He or she has not had a chance to be poisoned by naysayers and negative colleagues, but has simply gone out, done his or her best, and made the sales.

Too many times when we're trying to achieve something, we think there's a basic step-by-step, proven method we need to follow. By all means, we should study successful methods that have worked for others. But don't give up on an idea just because it seems to be something that hasn't been done before.

BIG DREAMS, BIG MOVES

Many times people do not succeed because they are not thinking big enough. We should always shoot for the highest heights. We limit ourselves because of the negatives other people have told us, and because of the negatives we have told ourselves. But why not shoot for the top? What's the worst that can happen?

After my radio talk show was on the air for about seven months, I decided to actively pursue my goal of syndicating the radio show and then taking the program to television. So I began making phone calls to many people, including the presidents of CNBC and Westwood One, two of the largest organizations in the radio and television industry. I called for several months. I didn't know these people. But I kept calling. Eventually, I got meetings with both. The president of CNBC said he finally saw me because I had been so nice to his assistant and established such a good rapport with her she finally convinced him to schedule an appointment. The president of Westwood One gave me an appointment when I finally caught him in the office at six-thirty at night, when he answered his own phone.

Then I told him that Infinity Broadcasting (his boss) had recommended I give him a call.

Neither one of those meetings resulted in a television show or the selection of my radio program for syndication. But they did result in a great deal of information for me. Each man gave me advice about what I needed to do to build up my experience. Each gave me qualified information that I could not have gotten from any book, or from trying to figure things out on my own.

There's no reason to be afraid to go to the highest sources possible. The most they can say is no. What is more likely is that you will come away with a large reservoir of information that will make your own path to the top a lot more effective. If they tell you you're not right for the job, or you don't have enough experience or the right credentials, ask them "What do I need to do to get enough experience or the right credentials?" Then ask, "If I go out and do the things you've suggested, can I come back and see you again?" If you shoot for the top, it's possible that you'll come away with massive amounts of information. If you shoot for the bottom, it's probable that you'll just get the dregs.

THE CALCULATED RISK

It's true that when you reach for the top, when you dream big dreams, you are taking a risk. There is no achievement in life without some form of risk. But there are ways to lessen the risk, to make it a "safer," more calculated risk.

What is it that eliminates or reduces risk? Basically, it is knowledge and experience. Suppose you were to decide that you wanted to be the next Evel Knievel. You line up twenty cars, build a makeshift ramp, get on a motorcycle, and off you go, ready to jump over them. The risks you are taking are enormous.

You could go another route. You could begin by becoming a professional motorcyclist. You could assemble an expert crew to help you build the most aerodynamically effective ramp possible. You could practice for months, first by jumping over one car, then two cars, then three, and so on. You could do this over and over again until you have perfected the twenty-car jump. By taking all of these steps (which are reminiscent of Kung Fu's concentrated effort), you have lessened the risk.

We take risks every day, from crossing the street, to driving a car, to getting on an airplane. We're willing to take these risks to get where we want to go. There are other risks we have to take in order to reach our goals. In his book *Success!* Michael Korda says:

Success does imply risks—the risk of new responsibilities, the risk of living up to new and greater expectations, the risk of losing what one has in the pursuit of what one wants. It is, however, important to recognize these fears as realistic, and to confront them in a sensible and organized way:

- Ask yourself how much responsibility you are prepared to take.
- Don't set your expectations so high that you are bound to fail.

- ◆ Assess just how willing you are to lose what you have in order to rise up the next step.

Once you have carefully and logically analyzed the risk factors, you can make an informed decision as to whether or not you want to go ahead with your plans, or make any modifications necessary in order that your goals will be more effectively reachable.

Jo Jerman of Merck, whom we met in Chapter 1, calls this "managed risk."

"I've done a fair amount of study on leadership," says Jerman. "One thing I consistently find when people describe a great leader is courage. You have to have enough courage and enough confidence in yourself and your abilities to really take a risk. I don't think that any great gains come without risk. I cannot see that the two can be separated.

"What you have to do is manage the risk. You have to look at your goals and say, 'What happens if I fall this short? What happens if I fall this much shorter?' In a corporation like mine, you have to manage the risk by letting the people around you know what might happen, and continually monitor the progress so you can make the risk more manageable."

Another leader who believes in taking risks is Ruth Simmons, president of Smith College and the first African-American woman to rise to that position at a top-ranked U.S. college. Simmons, the great-great-granddaughter of slaves, was born one of twelve children of a Texas sharecropper. However, she was brought up to do her best at everything she tried. She pursued her higher education majoring in romance languages, a field where there were almost no other African-Americans. In 1985, Simmons was asked to head the African-American studies program at Princeton. Many of her colleagues advised her against taking the position, saying she would be stereotyped within academia.

Simmons, however, believes that the key to her success is her willingness to take risks. She told Lauren Picker of *Parade* magazine (April 21, 1966), "If you are the kind of person who listens to conservative advice, you may do okay in life, but you probably won't ever be a fantastic leader. You have to take risks, and you also have to go against conventional wisdom, because conventional wisdom doesn't make for startling advances in society."

Not every act of courage involves making startling advances in society. For many of us, the most courageous acts involve stepping out into the unknown, away from the boundaries of the comfort zone in which we usually reside. It's uncomfortable to do something you've never done before, and it does take a certain amount of courage to get through it. But we've always been exposed to discomfort in our lives. When you go to a new school for the first time and have to walk into a room full of strangers, when you change jobs, go for an interview, take an exam, whenever you do something new, you're going to have a certain amount of fear. Courage is going forward in spite of that fear.

We've all had times when we've had to make a decision about whether to stay where we are or move onto a whole new ground. These decisions aren't easy. Our biggest fear is the fear of failure. We all remember the kid in class (or perhaps we were that kid) who knew the answers but was afraid to raise his or her hand because of the possibility of being wrong.

Successful people are afraid of failure, too. The difference is they understand that failure is the common denominator of success. Those who cope best accept their fear and move right through. If you wait for the fear to subside, you may be waiting forever. Psychologist Susan Jeffers, author of *Feel the Fear and Do It Anyway,* told *Cosmopolitan* (February 1995) that the trick is not to get rid of the fear, but to build up your confidence so that you can go forward despite it.

Says Jeffers: "What keeps us so petrified is mind talk that pulls us down—the nonstop little voice inside that says, 'You'd better not change your situation. There's nothing else out there for you. Don't take a chance.' The second you start thinking, Why should I even try for the job? I'll never get it, or What if he rejects me? what you immediately have to do is tell yourself, 'I'll handle it.' The fear of *not* being able to handle whatever happens is the main reason so many people remain stuck."

THERE'S ONLY ONE FIRST TIME

There are many people in this world who have little dreams. They don't start out as little dreams, but people make them little. Fear and doubt chip away at them until they're nothing more than fleeting memories and wishes of things that might have been.

There are choices that everyone makes in life. Some are easy, some are difficult. There will always be outside circumstances we can't control, but there are also decisions we can make about how we want to live our lives. We can choose to go through door number one, behind which we know lies a path of uncertainty and rough spots. Or we can choose door number two, which leads to a much gentler, easier road. Neither choice is right or wrong.

What's wrong is when you choose the easier road without ever having tried something new or different. Everybody has dreams of what they want to do in life, but some people spend large amounts of time making these dreams little. They keep them in a nice little box. They may take them out and look at them from time to time, but then they just sigh and stuff them right back into those safe little boxes.

What we don't think about is that there's only one first time. Once you take an action, it can never be quite as scary or difficult again. It's like Rita Rudner getting up on stage in front of a handful of drunken patrons at three in the morning. Those times were difficult, but she faced her fears and went on. Not only did she put the worst behind her, she learned something every time she stepped up to that microphone.

Every time we step up to try something we've never done before, we learn more than we expect. The uniqueness of the experience gives us insights we could never get except by taking an action. Why is it that children are such quick learners? It's because everything is new to them. They're experiencing everything for the first time. When we venture out into new worlds, we open our minds and our senses to things we might never otherwise experience. Our knowledge of the world expands tremendously with each new step we take.

When Olympic rower Carrie Graves was offered a coaching job at Harvard at the age of twenty-four, she had reservations about taking the job. She had never coached before, and there were very few women coaches in any sport, no less rowing. "They hired me even though I had no experience coaching, and I was about two years older than the kids I was coaching," says Graves. "Plus, for the two years previous to my coming, they had a male coach they absolutely adored."

The position didn't work very well for Graves the first year. The girls didn't like her. She was different; she wasn't the male coach they had had before. "By the second year, we were doing extremely well," says Graves, "even though that first year most of the people quit. It caused me a tremendous amount of self-doubt. But inside I always knew that I was right and that they were going to have to change. All the time, I was learning how to coach.

"I found out some years later my nickname was 'Old Stoneface' even though I was only twenty-four years old. I figured that since I didn't know what I was doing, and I was learning all the time, I just better keep my mouth shut. I wasn't going to say things that didn't make sense. I wasn't going to pretend I knew something when I didn't know it."

Graves learned several valuable lessons from this experience. First, she learned that she was capable of doing the job. Second, she learned that she was a risk taker, that she was not afraid of doing things her way, even if her way was different from what had been done before.

"I think I take risks because I'm not afraid to let information in," she says. "I'm not afraid to look at a situation and try a solution that hasn't been tried before. It helps me grow, and in coaching my team, it's going to help them. I look at all the information, all the data that I have. I'm not afraid, both as an athlete and as a coach, to make a change or to do something different—because it might work. I believe on an intuitive level that the greater the risk the greater the reward."

WHEN FAITH MEETS FEAR

Courage and fear are inevitably intertwined. We become courageous when faith meets fear, and we take action. When we believe strongly in what we're doing, and we're moving toward a goal that challenges all of our senses, we meet fear head-on. In most cases, fear serves a useful purpose. If we weren't afraid, we might plunge off a cliff without a parachute simply because it looked challenging. Fear forces us to take precautions.

But often fear limits us for no good reason. I believe that there is something deep down in every human being that yearns to find out what we're capable of doing, that longs to reach to our greatest potential. But we create prisons for ourselves when we limit our imagination with fear. When we make our dreams small, we make ourselves small. We don't need stones to break down our prison walls, we need a greater imagination and the courage to act upon our dreams. When we combine foresight and faith, organization, and concentrated effort, and splash it all with a sprinkle of courage, there is nothing we cannot achieve.

"In each age men of genius undertake the ascent. From below, the world follows them with their eyes. These men go up the mountain, enter the clouds, disappear, reappear. People watch them, mark them. They walk by the sides of precipices. They daringly pursue their road.

See them aloft, see them in the distance; they are but black specks. On they go. The road is uneven, its difficulties constant. At each step a wall, at each step a trap. As they rise the cold increases. They must make their ladder, cut the ice and walk on it, hewing the steps in haste. A storm is raging. Nevertheless they go forward in their madness. The air becomes difficult to breathe. The abyss yawns below them. Some fall. Others stop and retrace their steps; there is a sad weariness.

"The bold ones continue. They are eyed by the eagles; the lightning plays about them; the hurricane is furious. No matter, they persevere."

—VICTOR HUGO

five

Understanding

Everybody knows Dave Thomas. That is, everyone with a television set and/or a hunger for hamburgers. Dave Thomas is the founder and senior chairman of the board of Wendy's Old-Fashioned Hamburgers. The first Wendy's was opened in Columbus, Ohio, in 1956, named after Thomas's then eight-year-old daughter, Melinda Lou (nicknamed Wendy by her older brothers and sisters). Twenty-six years later there are more than five thousand Wendy's in the United States and thirty-four countries around the world, with sales over $4.5 billion.

Dave Thomas considers his greatest success to be his family. He's been married for more than forty years, and has five children and fourteen grandchildren. The reason family is so important to Thomas is that growing up he never had one of his own. He was born out of wedlock and was adopted. His adopted mother died when he was five years old; his foster father remarried three times. Thomas has been out on his own since the age of fifteen.

"I really know the value of family," says Thomas. "So that was one of my objectives in life, to be married and to have a family and to take care of my kids. I didn't know what to do when I had my first child. I remember looking at my daughter when she was two or three days old and thinking, What am I going to do now? How do I take care of and raise this little girl? I have five kids and sometimes I still wonder."

Thomas wanted his children to have a better life than he had. His adopted father was a construction worker who went from one job to the next, and Thomas often attended three or four different schools a year. He knew there was something different about his family. He would go to friends' homes, and see how they were treated by their parents. He knew he did not get that kind of treatment at home.

Dave Thomas came by his success the old-fashioned way: He earned it. He literally learned the restaurant business from the bottom up. There were two aspects to Thomas's business education: One was hard work in every facet of the business, and the other was finding mentors from whom he could learn.

"Mentoring is a very important thing," says Thomas. "There are so many people who will help you if you just ask. I was extremely inquisitive. I wanted to know, How do people become successful? I used to evaluate my mentors. My first job was working for two Greeks, gentlemen who came from the old country, in Knoxville, Tennessee. What I admired about those people was that there wasn't anything in the restaurant they wouldn't do. If they asked you to do something, they had already done it. I wanted to pattern my success after them, because I liked how they treated their people. They were very demanding; you had to work hard. I was only twelve years old. But I did learn how to work, and I learned what a work ethic really meant.''

LEARNING IS THE KEY

"When I asked executives how they learned and why they had been forced to reflect upon experience, you know what they often told me? Many had suffered through an unhappy marriage and divorce. In another case . . . , a daughter had committed suicide. It was amazing to me to see the extent to which personal hardships forced people to start, maybe for the first time, looking at their lives. Experiences like being fired, like having to fire people, like being demoted—these were the things people said they learned from.

"Because, you see, these things scream out for explanation. Learning men and women try to understand it. The people who don't learn . . . are not going to get very far in life.''

—WARREN BENNIS, FROM *REINVENTING LEADERSHIP*

We all suffer adversities in our lives. We all feel pressure of varying degrees. We all make mistakes and have to live with the consequences. But it is not the mistakes we make in life that hurt us. It is

111

not learning from those mistakes that leads to failure. The greatest gift we can give ourselves is the search for understanding.

Understanding is a combination of comprehension and personal interpretation. We must discover the facts behind the things that affect us, and then figure out what they mean to us.

Understanding is how we elevate ourselves toward success. Understanding gives us strength and courage. It gives us the confidence we need to put in the concentrated effort required to accomplish our goals. Through the understanding and the knowledge we gain over the years, interpretations of new information become magnified. In other words, every new thing we learn stands on the shoulders of everything else we've learned before.

If you go back and read a book you first read five years ago, you'll find you have a totally different appreciation and interpretation of the book now. That's because all the knowledge and experience you've accumulated in those five years gives you new insights that help you see things in a different light.

That's exactly what happened to Dr. Philip T. Santiago, New Jersey's Chiropractor of the Year for 1990 and a member of the medical staff for the U.S. Olympic team in the 1992 Barcelona games and the 1996 Olympic trials in Atlanta. When I first interviewed Dr. Santiago for *Diamond in the Rough,* he was at the pinnacle of success. He had recently returned from the Olympics, he had designed a highly successful course for doctors in sports medicine, and he was making more money with his practice than he had ever made before.

Then came overwhelming tragedy. Both Santiago's mother and father were killed in a car crash. It was a devastating blow to a close family. At the same time, managed health care began to have a big effect on people in his industry. He lost about 30 percent of his business and could not seem to get it back again. His world fell apart, and depression set in.

"I couldn't get out of it," says Santiago. "I lost the motivation of wanting to work. I started eating more and drinking more and not working out, doing all the bad things. Typical depression stuff. It took me more than two years to get myself back together."

There were a number of different factors that turned Santiago around. First, he began to study other people who had been successful, lost it all, and started all over again. He needed to be reassured that it could be done. He also wanted to surround himself with positive influences. So he picked up *Diamond in the Rough* and read it again.

"When I read all the stories of people who had gone through rough times and come out of it, I said, 'I can do that.' The first time I read the book, the stories were interesting, but they didn't have the same personal impact. This time I really knew what these people were talking about."

The second factor that started Santiago back on track was something that happened when he was at the Olympic trials in Atlanta. One of the head medical doctors for the team came up to him and said, "I really envy you."

"Why?" Santiago asked.

"Because when an athlete comes in with pain, you treat them with your hands. When you are done, they get up off the examination table and are out of pain.

I never get that kind of immediate satisfaction in treating patients."

"That got me thinking," says Santiago. "I realized what a gift my profession is to me. I realized I can do something not many doctors can do."

Santiago came back to his practice with a new attitude. He realized he needed a new understanding of his business in order to make it work. So he hired a new staff, people who really cared about the patients. He decided that the only way to beat the managed care problem was to offer people such excellent service that they would be willing to pay more for it. His practice is now at a higher level than it ever was before the adversity struck.

"What I learned was that what I wanted most was to create a legacy. I grew up always wanting to please my parents as a person and proud as being top in the chiropractic profession. They're not here anymore, but I know they can still see me, and I want to do my best for them. And when I have children, I want them to have a legacy that they can carry on to the next generation."

When Dr. Santiago read *Diamond in the Rough* for the second time, he identified with many of the stories he found there. When you read this book and the information it contains, when you read the quotes and the stories from people who have gone through great adversity, you will inevitably compare these situations to your own life and your own challenges. Some information and some stories will have more meaning for you than others because of how they compare to your own experience. But they all offer a way to find a deeper understanding of how to get through life's challenges.

Experience and action must always be accompanied by understanding. When we're lost, when we're depressed, when we are discouraged and can't find a way out, it is understanding that leads us back to solid ground. Through research, through reading, through talking to other people who have been there before us, we gain the knowledge and insights we need to get us on track once again. We realize that we have been misinterpreting a situation, or that we can do more than we have been doing, or simply that others have survived the same and worse.

The quest for knowledge is part of being human. We want to know how things work, why things happen, what we can do to change things. But knowledge in itself is useless; it is the application of that knowledge that allows us to soar.

"There are many truths of which the full meaning cannot be realized until personal experience has brought it home."

—JOHN STUART MILL

We must apply what we learn. If we don't, all we get is theoretical jargon that sits on a page or flies off into thin air and is no help to anyone. We must consume information every day that will lead us toward our goals and aspirations.

There are three basic aspects of understanding that can help alleviate pressure and overcome adversity. They are

- Understanding stress and pressure
- Becoming an "expert" in your field
- Learning from others

UNDERSTANDING STRESS AND PRESSURE

There is an old saying that goes "One man's meat is another man's poison." When you're talking about stress, the saying is "One man's stress is another man's motivator." A situation or event that is stressful to one person might be a creative challenge to another. Even within ourselves, stress changes daily. Most stress experts agree that stress comes from within—the same late train or annoying phone call will bother us one day, and the next day we will take it in stride, calmly or even humorously. Why? Because stressors are always out there to aggravate us if we let them. It is *how* we react to stressors that makes the difference. We can, therefore, control our stress with greater awareness, understanding, and desire.

"Pressure is perceived differently by every person," Dr. Jeff Kahn, a New York psychologist, told *Sales and Marketing Management* magazine (April 1997). "How people deal with pressure is determined by how they view the circumstances around them. If they fully understand the expectations and recognize what type of environment they're working in, then they'll be able to face the pressure."

Stress can be both positive and negative. Stress can trigger an energy level that enables us to perform at our highest capacity. On the other hand, too much stress can produce extreme anxiety and even a paralysis of action. Stress is a necessary force to achieve optimum performance. In general, people react badly to either too little or too much stress.

If you have too few demands on you, you experience boredom and frustration. If there are too many demands on you, you get overloaded, you have difficulty concentrating, and you ultimately experience burnout. In the middle ground, when stress is present but not overwhelming, you are stimulated, alert, creative, and decisive.

According to Richard S. Moore of Anglia Polytechnic University in England, "The 'stress' which people complain about, or makes them function less well, is a feeling of tension or pressure experienced when they feel that the demands placed on them (stressors) exceed the resources they have to meet them."

When those demands become overwhelming, it is time to go back to FOCUS. We must go back and ask ourselves focusing questions: Where are we going? What are we trying to accomplish? Whom are we trying to benefit? How are we organized? How are we concentrating our efforts? When we become confused and anxious, it's because we've lost our focus. When we lose focus, we give up. When we experience the stress that obstacles and adversity present, and look for the lessons learned, we can return stress to its optimum level.

Robert Sapolsky, professor of biology and neuroscience at the University of Pennsylvania and author of *Why Zebras Don't Get Ulcers,* says that people who cope best with stress and pressure are people who can distinguish well between the time the stressful event is going on and when it isn't. "They don't have anticipatory stress," says Sapolsky. "And they don't spend hours or days afterward obsessing over it. When they need it they turn it on, the rest of the time they turn it off."

Sapolsky tells of a study that was done concerning air traffic controllers. One would expect people in that profession to have a host of stress-related diseases. But when the most successful controllers (those who lasted in the profession and were rated by their peers as being best at their jobs) were studied, they were found to be just as hypertensive and hyperventilated as everyone else during their work time. Yet two minutes before and two minutes afterward, unlike the others, they were thinking about the baseball game or what they would be having for dinner.

We can't eliminate stress from our lives. But we can cope with it, and keep it at manageable levels. Here are six ways to manage the pressure in your life:

Take a step back.   The worst thing you can do is make important decisions when you're under tremendous pressure. If at all possible, take time to evaluate the situation, and review the long- and short-term consequences of any decision you make.

Clarify your values and relationships.   Remember what's most important to you. Pressure sometimes tempts us to take shortcuts or make unethical decisions we wouldn't normally make. Only through introspection can you discover what really matters to you—and then act on it.

Seek and establish a balance.   Find the middle ground between the inner you, the work-related you, the spiritual you—all the various roles you play. A workaholic is not in balance, nor is someone who plays all the time.

Practice your communication skills. Many times, a great deal of confusion and frustration can be relieved simply by talking things over with people you trust. Talk to people who can help you. Sometimes other people can be objective when you can't. They may come up with solutions to help alleviate the pressure.

Analyze your environment. W. Clement Stone once said: "You are a product of your environment. So choose the environment that will best develop you toward your objective. . . . Are the things around you helping you toward success—or are they holding you back?" If they are holding you back, evaluate how you can make changes in your environment—or move to a different one.

Take action. Pressure intensifies the more we dwell on it. As soon as we take some action, even the smallest, we feel more in control and begin to have hope that there is a light at the end of the tunnel.

BECOMING AN "EXPERT" IN YOUR FIELD

In the context of adversity, the object of obtaining knowledge is to eliminate fear. The more we know about something, the less fearful it becomes. You'll find that successful people don't have any less fear than anyone else, they just have more knowledge. They know their business inside out. We attack fear—we overwhelm it—by becoming an expert in our field of endeavor.

In *Diamond in the Rough* I talked about FEAR: False Evidence Appearing Real. We are often afraid of what we *think* will happen to us in a new situation. These fears are not based on fact, they are based on imagination. And imagination is a powerful force. Used for visualizing a positive outcome, it can give you a tremendous boost toward achieving your goal. But used for hypothesizing negative events, it can stop you from pursuing your dreams.

That's why it's imperative to learn as much fact as you possibly can. If you want to be the best guitarist in the world, for instance, here are two things that need to be done: One is to practice, practice, practice. The second is to study the instrument, study different styles of music, study the masters who have played the guitar throughout the years. You also need to study the music industry, find out how it works, and how you can become a part of that world. This intensive research can be done in any field you might want to pursue.

Recently, a survey was taken of more than nine thousand millionaires. One of the traits they all had in common was an enormous amount of reading, usually business-related. They invested themselves and their time in their profession. It didn't matter if they had graduated from college or were high-school dropouts, they found that the knowledge they gained from studying their profession not only helped them get ahead, but helped them find creative solutions for the people around them.

Universal truth and knowledge are out there if only people would look and listen. It amazes me how many people do not take advantage of the knowledge that surrounds them. Nightingale-Conant is the largest producer of business-oriented motivational tapes in the country. About a decade ago, they realized that they were hitting only about 5 percent of the population, people who were already interested in becoming high achievers. They wondered how they could get to the other 95 percent of the population. They put together a huge and well-thought-out advertising campaign, and spent millions of dollars trying to get to that elusive 95 percent. What happened? The more money they spent, the more they advertised, the more they learned and improved the campaign—the more the original 5 percent bought.

EXCUSES, EXCUSES

What happens to the other 95 percent? What is it that keeps them from pursuing their dreams? It all comes back to "False Evidence Appearing Real." It is an anticipation of negative results, imagination working overtime. People are afraid of failing, afraid they will make a mistake, afraid they will look foolish. "False Evidence Appearing Real" is the reason we believe the excuses we make for ourselves. Therefore, the first step in taming any fear is to analyze what is real and what is not. Then dive in and take action.

In order to take action, we have to learn to get rid of our fear of failure. Author Tom Peters tells about how he had the privilege of introducing the late Sam Walton, the founder of Wal-Mart, when he was going to be inducted into the Sales and Marketing Executives Hall of Fame.

"What can you say in two minutes about a guy like Walton?" says Peters. "I called David Glass, CEO of Wal-Mart. I said, 'If you had ninety seconds to say something about Sam Walton, what would you say?' Quicker than a wink, he answered, 'Sam Walton is not afraid to fail. He'll give something a try, he'll make a total mess of it, and walk back in tomorrow with a smile on his face and another idea.' It's that ability to try something, make a mess of it, and get on with the next action that allows us to win out over fear."

The key to this book is to understand that everyone experiences fear and failure. Billionaire Morty Davis was a quiet young man who was "scared out of his mind" to do anything in public. Determined to succeed in life, he attended Harvard Business School. The first day of school, he was told that 10 percent of his class would flunk out, and he was sure he would be among that group.

"I was from Brooklyn," he says, "and everybody else had British, Australian, and beautiful Southern accents. I thought they were all geniuses." His brother, who had gone to Harvard before him, told him that those people who spoke up in class did best. The first day of classes, one of his professors said, "Does anybody want to volunteer to speak?" Davis, despite his heavy Brooklyn accent and his insecurity, volunteered.

"It's overcoming that fear that makes me successful," he says. "I'm just as reluctant to get rejected today when I make a cold sales call, or when I do anything. You get rejected by clients, you get rejected by relatives . . . The president of this country usually wins by about 51 percent. That means almost half the country dislikes him. Even the half that vote for him are usually voting against the guy they don't like. Everyone gets rejected. The only way to keep going is to get a better frame of reference."

Some people, listening to Morty Davis's story, will say, "Sure he had it rough. But after all, look at where he went to school. He's probably had it easy since then, with all his Harvard connections." They don't know that he was a high school dropout and a teenage juvenile delinquent. They don't know about the many jobs he had before he got into Harvard, including delivering milk bottles on cold predawn mornings where his fingers froze; becoming a diamond cutter's apprentice and working until his hands were bloody and callused; and selling vacuum cleaners door-to-door and getting rejection after rejection. They don't know that he and his family had to leave Harvard before his graduation ceremonies because they couldn't afford the extra week's rent it would have taken to stay. All they see is a successful man, and they say, "I can never get ahead, because I don't have his connections."

Excuses keep us from going after even those things we'd most like to do. During a recent extended conversation with a talented acquaintance whose hobby is painting, he told me that he would like to do more with his art, but, he said, "there are so many starving artists out there."

Excuses. We hear them all the time. We probably use some of them ourselves. For instance:

"There's too much competition."   The answer to that is, there really is no competition. People may do the same thing you do. They may have the same, or similar, goals as you. That is true—on the surface. The underlying truth is that no two people are the same, not even twins. What you bring to the table is going to be unique. You need to learn to emphasize your unique qualities and let people know what sets you apart from others in your field.

The only competition you really face is yourself. Can you do better than you've done before? Can you beat your own record? When your focus is on what someone else is doing, you diminish your own chances at success. You should study the competition only to understand what they are doing, and what "customers" like and dislike about them, so you can then evaluate your own performance and make changes to improve. You will succeed when you change your focus from competing with others to learning from them and creating from within yourself.

Another suggestion is to embrace your competition. I have a competitor who became a good friend, named Tony Parinello. He gives terrific sales training seminars on how to get to top decision makers. He and I are in the same business. Yet I often call him to talk, ask his advice, and share ideas. He gives me leads, and I give him leads. We have similar products and services that we're marketing. We have the same customers and same audiences; we compete for the same dollars. But the love we have for our products, the love we have for what we do, and the love we have for each other brings us together to share ideas. We know that we can benefit each other. To me, competition is companionship.

"I haven't got time."   We've got all the time in the world. The question to ask is "What are we doing with that time?" We can't always do everything we need or want to do every day. Organizing your time is a matter of priorities. It means reviewing your goals, every day if necessary, and asking, "What do I need to do today to get closer to my goal? How can I break my day down into time slots so that I can get these three (or four or five) important things done?"

When we say we don't have time, we're not always aware of how much time we waste. How much time do you spend watching television each day? Or playing computer games? There's nothing wrong with relaxing and having leisure time. But if you were to ask people who have one year to live how much time they spend watching television, they would tell you it was a very small portion of their day. The first step to take when you find yourself saying, "I don't have time," is to keep track of exactly how you spend your day now. You'll be surprised at how much time you have available to you.

You don't have to have large chunks of time available to accomplish your goals. If you can't manage large chunks, try several smaller chunks. Fifteen minutes a day, one hour a week, one day a month— however you can work it out. The most important thing is to get started. If you're really passionate about reaching your goal, you'll find ways to expand the amount of time available to you.

Nothing in life is accomplished without sacrifice. You may have to sacrifice one thing to accomplish another. You may have to sacrifice some time with your family; you may have to work on a weekend or a holiday. When you do that in pursuit of a worthy goal, your leisure time becomes even more valuable to you. When you work hard and accomplish something, you earn your time off and enjoy it even more. Then you can truly relax, without thinking, I should be doing this, I should have done that.

> *"Everything has a price. Whatever we want in life, we must give up something to get it. The greater the value, the greater the sacrifice required. There is a high price to pay for success. But we must realize that the rewards of true success are well worth the effort. The highway to success is a toll road."*
> —FROM *THE BEST OF SUCCESS*, COMPILED BY WYNN DAVIS

"I'm too old." President Bush, at the age of seventy-two, made his first parachute jump from a plane. Some people probably told him that he was too old to do that. He obviously disagreed. There are thousands of stories of people who retired from their corporate jobs in their sixties or seventies and then went on to accomplish great things in their later years. Scientists have recently shown that the brain is a "use it or lose it" muscle; if we continue to stimulate the muscle into our later years, the probability of developing Alzheimer's and other age-related brain disorders lessens considerably.

There are realities that must be dealt with, however. I know someone who is in her late sixties. She is on social security and looking for part-time work. She has come back from many an interview convinced that she didn't get the job because she was too old. She may be right. Employers often think that younger people will be less expensive to hire and easier to train. There are many prejudices against senior citizens. In that case, you need to emphasize the advantages of being older: experience and wisdom.

"I'm too young." Young people suffer from the opposite problems of the elderly. They often believe they don't have enough knowledge or experience to go after their dreams; they suffer from insecurity and lack of confidence.

For example, my sister-in-law, new to the pharmaceuticals industry, was recently scheduled to give a speech to a roomful of doctors. She was nervous about the fact that she was new to the industry, and new to speaking in public. She didn't want her inexperience to come out in her speech. When she asked me for advice, I told her to find the most respected doctor in the field of the doctors to whom she was going to speak. I told her to call him up and say, "I need your help. I'm going to speak to a group of doctors like yourself, and I'm wondering if you can make my job easier by telling me how you would do it if you were making the presentation to your colleagues. What would you emphasize in the presentation?"

She did just that. Her presentation was highly successful because she did not come across as an inexperienced newcomer; she had the information and the backing of someone highly respected in the field.

Sometimes the innocence and enthusiasm of youth work in your favor. People are often willing to help out a newcomer—they remember their own shaky beginnings and want to help others just getting started. There is also something to be said for naïveté and inexperience. Jim McCann, founder of 1-800-FLOWERS, says, looking back ten years ago to when he bought the company, "If I knew then what I know now, I never would have done the deal. I'm glad I was pretty dumb then. We made the mistake of making the purchase, and we made the best of it. In fact, we made a huge success of it."

"I have too many responsibilities." When I wanted to go into business for myself, I asked my father-in-law, who had built his own business from the ground up, if he thought this was the right time for me. His answer? "There never is a 'right time.' The right time is when you really want to do it. The longer you wait, the greater the barriers become. If you wait for your kids to graduate, other things may come up. You don't know what the future holds."

There are many people who say, "I'd like to pursue my dreams right now, but I have too many responsibilities. I have a family to support, my kids are in college and I have a mortgage to pay." They're right. They do have those responsibilities. That doesn't mean they have to give up their dreams entirely. When I started my training and seminar business, I still had a full-time job. I put together proposals and looked for new clients evenings, weekends—whenever I could spare a moment. Slowly but surely, I built up a client base, until I could go out on my own.

We spend a lot of time trying to sell ourselves out of taking action, and convincing ourselves it's not the right time. Even if it's not the right time, it's still the best time. By using the FOCUS acronym, you can start a little bit at a time. Have the foresight to imagine where you want to go, and the faith that you can make it happen. Organize yourself. Set goals, write out a plan, outline the steps you'll need to take. Concentrate your efforts. Be courageous and accept that risk is part of the game. Understand what it is you're going into. Learn everything you can about the business or the field you want to enter. Start seeding (which we'll talk about in the next chapter)— use all your connections to let everyone know about your new endeavor. With all these elements in place, you will succeed.

"I couldn't do that."   We've all had this reaction at some point in our lives. A friend says something like, "You're a wonderful cook. You should write a cookbook," or "You'd make a terrific public speaker," or "You write very well. You should try to publish some of your stories." Your reply? "Oh, I couldn't do that!"

What is it that's stopping you? Fear of the unknown. Fear of failure. Any of the above excuses. False Evidence Appearing Real.

Instead of letting your initial reaction, which is based on fear, make the decision for you, why not say instead, "That's interesting. I wonder what would happen if I tried that."

Ask anyone who has achieved success, and they'll tell you they had the same "I couldn't do that" initial reaction. But they set a goal and accomplished it, and you can do the same.

THE ACTION SOLUTION

"The common conception is that motivation leads to action, but the reverse is true—action precedes motivation. You have to 'prime the pump' and get the juices flowing, which motivates you to work on your goals. Getting momentum going is the most difficult part of the job, and often taking the first step . . . is enough to prompt you to make the best of your day."

—W. CLEMENT STONE

All these excuses are external reactions to internal fear. If we allow them to permeate our thoughts, they will permeate our actions—or rather lack of actions. Excuses keep us from taking action. The longer we put off taking action, the stronger the fear and the excuses become. There is no guarantee that you will succeed at everything you try; the only guarantee is the failure that comes with never having tried at all.

If you face fear and walk right through it, you can explode it. Tom Peters's advice for getting through fear, rising out of depression, or pushing oneself out of inertia, is to "take any action at all. Quit wallowing. It doesn't matter whether you go out for a five-mile jog, play a sport, or make a follow-up call to someone you made a sale to last week. Just don't sit there."

Inaction has a way of stretching itself out, says Peters. "I've had times where one day of inaction stretched into two days, then into three. We've all had these times of despair. The only answer is to get back on the horse immediately and do something. Suddenly you discover that you are, in fact, able to stand up again on your own two feet. We act our way into success, rather than thinking our way into success.

"The world is a hopelessly complicated place. You have to get out there into the fray, take your lumps, get up and try a new idea tomorrow. That doesn't mean you always do it with a smile on your face. Getting whacked on the side of the head may cause a few tears. But that's life. The number one cause of failure is not that someone has tried something that didn't work out. The number one cause of failure is not taking action at all."

The more action we take, the more we understand that our imagination is often stronger than reality. What we perceive to be a barrier sometimes turns out to be only a mirage.

Success depends upon taking action. There are people in this world Calvin Coolidge called "educated derelicts." They have walls full of degrees and diplomas, yet they never accomplish much. Then there are those who never got beyond high school, who had confidence in themselves and had faith in their dreams, who were persistent and undeterred by setbacks and obstacles. Those are the people who achieve success.

Lee Blowstein is an action-oriented person whose philosophy of life is "Stuff happens." Blowstein, now a top distributor with a major international network marketing company, had at one time built up a large business on his own. Then times, technology, and the economy changed, and he had to start all over again.

"Everybody has a dream," says Blowstein. "But before the dream has a chance of coming true, you have to wake up. Recently I was talking to a group of people and I asked, 'Who here would like to be financially successful?' Everyone raised their hand. Then I asked, 'What have you done to achieve that goal? What did you do today, last week, last month?' Most of the people just sat there and looked at me. We all have dreams, but only those who are not afraid to act on them will achieve success."

LEARNING FROM OTHERS

You can learn a lot from research and studying. You can learn a lot from action and experience. There is one more important method of soliciting feedback and finding ways to improve, and that is by developing a network of mentors who can give you help, support, and constructive criticism. Everyone should have at least five mentors in his or her life, including family, friends, colleagues, and peers. Anyone whose judgment you respect can be a mentor, as long as he or she does not possess the following qualities:

- Mentors should not be people who have a negative attitude, who try to put you down and pull you down because you're trying to do something unique or unusual.

- They should not be people who think you can do no wrong, and who might have difficulty giving you constructive advice.
- They should not be people who are anxious to tell you how they, or someone they know, failed at just the thing you are trying to do. If you want to know how to fail at something, find someone who failed and they'll teach you their "success." If you want to learn success, find someone who is successful and they'll share their knowledge and experience with you.

We are often afraid to ask for advice or assistance, but are just as often surprised by people's willingness to help. People are usually glad to be able to help. For instance, I recently approached Morty Davis and asked him to be a mentor. Instead of citing lack of time or any of the other excuses you might imagine, Davis said, "Yes, of course. I take that as a compliment." He also offered to help me make some contacts and gave me advice on how to market the Barry J. Farber radio show.

Here's what four other highly successful people had to say about mentors:

Dave Thomas, founder and CEO of Wendy's: "There are mentors everywhere, although you may have to search them out. There are plenty of classy people out there who want to help. Instead of waiting for someone to take you under his wing, go out and find a good wing to climb under. People who are successful love to share. All you have to do is learn to listen. There are so many people out there who would love to give you information."

Barbara Mandrell, country western superstar: "It's vitally important to have mentors. Some of mine were Patsy Cline, George Jones, and June Carter—and especially my dad. When I look back, there were many people who were very generous to me. These people live by the idea of giving back a little bit of what's given to you."

Josh Weston, chairman of ADP: "I'd like to redefine 'mentor' somewhat. Most people think of a mentor as a singular coach who helps them through thick and thin. For me, it's more about being an extremely interactive person. I visit every single ADP facility and try to speak with everyone there. So I guess I might indirectly be a mentor to thousands by making myself present and accessible and not just sitting behind a closed door on the fiftieth floor of a skyscraper. I've always found it's very valuable to a company to get all your people to interact, at all levels. Not only with clients and customers, but also with people in their industry and elsewhere, sharing ideas from which they might learn."

***Geoffrey Brewer, executive editor of* Sales and Marketing Management** *magazine:* "It's very important to have mentors—but it's important to mentor others as well. When you take people under your wing and help develop them, you also learn from them, you get refreshed and you get new ideas. You also realize how much you know, so it can be a good confidence-builder."

Look for mentors everywhere in life—at work and in your personal life. But don't sit around and wait for others to help you—take action and you will get the help, and the feedback, you need.

LEARNING FROM YOURSELF

Mentors can be of great help in times of adversity. But you can't rely totally on others to help get you through. When communications consultant Dorothy Leeds found out she had cancer several years ago, she went through a major reassessment of her life.

"You have to keep growing mentally and emotionally," she says. "At the end of each year, you should ask, 'What did I learn this year? Which relationships did I improve?' You have to give yourself feedback, stop and assess where you've been and what you have to do next. You should do whatever you can spiritually to keep yourself peaceful, optimistic, open to the universe and all the good things that are out there. You have to learn from your mistakes, and learn to recover quickly. Staying grounded in morass and misery is not going to help. You have to try to move out of bad times as reasonably and as quickly as possible."

Sometimes it takes tough decisions to move out of bad times, and you may have to take action quickly. How can you help that process along? Jo Jerman of Merck & Company is often faced with tough situations in her highly competitive pharmaceuticals industry. In order to make tough decisions, Jerman uses a three-pronged approach.

"First, I collect as much high-quality data as I can in the shortest amount of time. If I have longer, I go for in-depth information, but if not, I go to the sources I know can give me the best data as fast as possible.

"Second, I go to the smartest people I can find who work for me or with me. I present the situation, the data I have collected, and then ask them to give me their responses, ideas, and feedback. I also try to find out if they've run into similar situations, and if so, how did they handle them.

"The third thing I do is use my gut. If you ignore your gut feelings, you ignore a fundamental factor of success. Every major leader in every walk of life, from military leaders to CEOs to entrepreneurs, has to make tough decisions and make them fast. And some of those decisions have to come from the gut level.

"If you combine these factors—objective information, feedback from others, and your own natural instincts—you can get through the most difficult times."

Another method of getting through adversity is to rely on the strengths you learned and earned from your own background and experiences. Jim McCann of 1-800-FLOWERS was a social worker before he went into the flower field.

"People kid me all the time and say how can you be a business-person running a company that has several thousand people working for it, involved in the floral business. You weren't born in the flower business like so many people in that industry are," says McCann. "What I tell them is that the training I had running a home for teenage boys, kids who had confronted real adversity in their lives, was a terrific training ground for the business career I have today and for the industry I'm involved in. There were challenges I confronted then, working with ten teenage boys who were not particularly motivated. They were involved in gunfights, rapes, gang assaults. Those kids had to confront those things every day. Working in that environment, by extension I did, too.

"In confronting those situations you learn to adapt quickly. And you learn what you're good at and what you're not good at. I'm here to tell you that those years working in that profession were the best training ground I could possibly have had for my life and for business. It teaches you how to pierce veils of protection that we put around ourselves that don't give us the opportunity for the social interaction that we all strive for.

"The biggest challenge I have today is to not dwell on mistakes I've made. Often in an interview I'm asked 'What is the single biggest mistake you've made?' I say the biggest mistake anyone can make is to spend time thinking about mistakes you've made. It doesn't do you any good. Go on. The best thing you can do is recover, and recover quickly. People who dwell on their mistakes become overly cautious and won't take challenges, won't take risks in the future. I think that's the single biggest mistake we can all make—to confront adversity and then shrink from opportunities in the future."

"Blessed is the man who finds wisdom, and the man who gets understanding, for the gain from it is better than gain from silver and its profit better than gold. It is more precious than diamonds; nothing you desire can compare with it."

—PROVERBS 3:13–15

six

Seeding
and Service

ONE OF THE most important aspects of learning to deal with adversity and failure is understanding the law of averages. There are many people in the world who aim, aim, aim—and never fire. They stop just at the point when they might have a chance at success. Their fear of failure is so great, they never take the shot. Therefore, they can never be successful.

The law of averages says that if you keep shooting, eventually you'll hit something. Nothing happens until the activity begins, until you get out there and start hitting those barriers. The more you expose yourself to new and different things, the more opportunities you'll run into, and the better your chances of success.

This is the philosophy Don Levine lives by, only his phrase for it is "Fate is a hunter." In other words, when fate comes around to seek you out, you'd better be ready to seize the opportunity.

You might not recognize the name Don Levine. But you will recognize the name of his most famous creation: GI Joe. In 1959, the Mattel company came out with the Barbie doll, which of course became a huge success. In 1963, Don Levine (who now owns DML Associates, which develops and markets products for major toy companies) was working for Mattel's rival, Hasbro Toys. Levine and his colleagues were anxious to get in on the "razor/razor blade philosophy." Once you bought a razor (this was before disposables were invented), you had to keep buying the special blades that fit. Once you bought a Barbie doll, you had to go out and buy all her new clothes and accessories. Hasbro wanted a doll along those lines, but didn't want to go directly against the Barbie phenomenon.

So Don Levine came up with the idea of a soldier that would have lots of accessories that children (or their parents) could buy. He also coined the term "action figure." That's because industry buyers were convinced that boys wouldn't buy dolls—after all, they didn't buy Barbie's boyfriend, Ken—girls did. But Levine was convinced that boys would buy into the idea of an action figure. Apparently he was right; in over thirty years, more than 400 million GI Joes have been sold.

It was an uphill task to convince buyers that GI Joe would sell. But that was nothing compared with Don Levine's pre-Hasbro experiences. He was working for a company that made scrapbooks, notebooks, and other traditional stationery items. It was the 1950s, and both Levine's wife and daughter were wearing ponytails. Levine suggested to his boss that they do a line of stationery items with a ponytail theme. The boss was skeptical. "What we've been doing has worked for thirty years. Why change now?" he said.

Still, Levine believed in his idea. He showed sketches to some salespeople and buyers, all of whom agreed it was a great concept. But when he went back to his boss with this added support, Levine was quickly handed a pink slip and fired.

Although he had a growing family to support, Levine did not give up. He joined up with a small company that believed in his idea. They convinced Woolworth's to give them an order. Woolworth's agreed to stock Ponytail products in twenty of its two thousand stores. If sales went well after two weeks, they would expand their order.

Levine did not just sit back and wait to see what would happen. He knew that fate is a hunter, and he had to be out there where fate could find him. So he took the last of his money and flew to each of the twenty Woolworth stores. He stood outside handing $20 bills to passersby, asking them to go in and buy a Ponytail product. Ten days later, Levine and his small company had an order for all two thousand Woolworth stores and Ponytail was on its way.

SEEDING THE LANDSCAPE

"He who obtains has little. He who scatters has much."
—LAO-TZU

Every farmer knows that in order to get a good-sized crop to grow, you must plant a lot of seeds. The farmer knows that not all seeds will sprout. Some will get eaten by birds or insects. Some will dry up in the hot sun; others will get washed away in the rain. This is to be expected. If the farmer planted only one seed, everything—the farmer's entire livelihood—would depend on that one plant.

So the farmer plants hundreds of seeds, nurtures them as best he or she can, and knows that some will not survive the season. But the farmer also knows that taking care of the land, providing fertilizer and water, will mean many seeds survive, and there will surely be a crop come fall.

That is what seeding is all about. A great idea that never comes to light helps no one. A worthy goal that is never acted upon is of no use. It takes activity, and lots of it, to make anything happen. When you're attempting to get something accomplished, you may try a lot of things that don't work out. You may hit dead ends. That's okay. You've learned which routes don't work for you. You may call on a lot of people who can't help you. But maybe, by making all those calls, you'll come across that one person who can't help you directly, but who knows someone who knows someone who is married to a person whose cousin in Topeka has just the solution you're looking for.

Here are a few suggestions to help make seeding work for you:

Make sure you've got the garden covered.   Many times we throw out a few seeds here and there and simply hope for the best. We've got to make sure we've covered all corners of the plot. Someone may give you a lead that seems like a long shot. It might be, but if you don't follow up, you'll never find out. You have to be prepared for failure, but don't convince yourself of it before you even try.

Lee Blowstein, the top distributor with a major international network marketing company, is an expert "farmer." His business was built on seeding. "I will talk to anybody," says Blowstein. "Of course, not everybody offers the same possibilities. You have to make judgments in any business. It's as if I had a billion-dollar business and I was hiring a general manager at three hundred thousand dollars a year. I may have to interview three hundred people before I find the person that I want. Still, I would interview all those people because you never know which one of them is going to be the one you need."

Don't give up just before the miracle. At the end of the day when you're ready to close up shop, shut down the computer, pull the blinds, and go home—don't. Make one more phone call. Put in one more half hour of work. Read one more magazine article about your industry. Know that doing these things will bring you that much closer to your dreams.

Learn from seeds that don't germinate. Every time you plant a seed that doesn't grow, learn something from its development. If this was not the right soil, did you get advice as to where else you might plant? Don't forget to evaluate how you went about planting the seed. Did you take the other person's needs into consideration? Were you asking for help without being willing to give anything in return? Maybe you were trying to plant at the wrong time of the year. We can't always get what we want just when we want it. Perhaps you can try again when the contact is more receptive.

Ask others to help you seed. You're not asking them to do your work for you. But every time you connect with someone, ask that person if he or she knows anyone else that you might contact. If the person does, be sure to contact those people, and mention the source of your connection ("I just spoke with Professor Jones and she told me you were an expert in this field . . ."). Don't forget to thank everyone you contact. Even if someone wasn't able to help, you might want to drop him or her a short note saying thanks for speaking with you. You're not just planting seeds for one particular crop, but for future crops as well.

Take pleasure in the process. To me, the whole process of seeding is a joyful experience. There's a special delight that comes when you uncover one opportunity after the other and you're moving toward your goal. That's when I'm happiest, right in the middle of that process—not when I reach my goal, or when I'm in the planning stages, but when I'm planting my garden and activity is going on and things are getting done.

There's also that great sense of curiosity about the future. There's probably some anxiety mixed in there, too, because we don't know what's going to happen, but there's also the awe and excitement of wondering what the fruits of our labor will look like. That eagerness to know the outcome often pulls us through when we're tired and cranky and thinking we can't go on. But we do go on, because we want to know the end of the story.

MAKING THE CONNECTION

Today, everyone has connections. Technology such as the Internet has made it possible for us to get expert help on almost any subject in an instant. Even if we don't find the exact information we need on the Net, we can usually find out who has the information we need. Don't forget how much people like being asked to share their knowledge. If you're not convinced, read this passage from *Bird by Bird* by Anne Lamott:

> There are an enormous number of people out there with invaluable information to share with you, and all you have to do is pick up the phone. They love it when you do, just as you love it when people ask if they can pick your brain about something you happen to know a great deal about—or, as in my case, have a number of impassioned opinions on. Say you happen to know a lot about knots, or penguins, or cheeses, and the right person asks you to tell him or her everything you know. What a wonderful and rare experience. Usually what happens in real life is that people ask you questions you can't remember the answer to, like what you came into the kitchen to get, or what happened on the Fourth of July in 1776, and you sit there thinking, "God, I knew that; it's right there on the tip of my tongue. . . ." When you do actually know a bit about something, it is such a pleasure to be asked a lot of questions about it.

Remember, too, that no matter how much technology affords us, it will never replace human contact. Super sports agent Marc

Roberts and author of *Roberts Rules* (Career Press, 1998) knows the value of the human touch, in the extremely competitive sports management arena where relationships are everything. Marc will fly across the country just to shake a client's hand and meet face-to-face, even if it's just for five minutes. There is no replacement for face-to-face contact.

Making connections also means knowing how to seed so that you set up win-win situations for yourself and all other parties. For instance, I recently set up a meeting between one of my best clients, Val-Pak, and Nightingale-Conant, producer of the *Diamond in the Rough* audio program. Val-Pak sends coop mailings to millions of people all over the country. Nightingale-Conant is a hundred-million-dollar company producing personal development products who've featured *Diamond in the Rough* on the cover of their catalog. By connecting them and Val-Pak, I not only gave these companies the opportunity to help each other's business, I also increased the advertisement possibilities for my own book. It was a win-win-win situation. That's what makes this kind of networking valuable.

Everyone you come in contact with has goals and customers of his or her own. So when I work with clients, I always try to ask myself, "Who are their clients? Who are they trying to sell to? What are their goals?" I try to help them reach those goals. If I can put two contacts or two vendors together, or a vendor of mine with one of my clients to help them increase their business, that allows us all to win. My clients see me as someone looking out for their best interest, and many times the vendor that I hook up with my client ends up giving me business or refering me to someone else. Everyone wins.

KEEP THE MOMENTUM GOING

"People who say that life is not worthwhile are really saying that they themselves have no personal goals which are worthwhile. . . . Get yourself a goal worth working for. Better still, get yourself a project. . . . Always have something ahead of you to 'look forward to'—to work for and hope for."

—MAXWELL MALTZ

After you experience any kind of success, it is very tempting to sit back on your heels and spend time congratulating yourself. After all, you have just successfully accomplished a goal. But it isn't in your best interest to just sit back. Instead, the best thing you can do is begin immediately working toward another goal. Why? Because, as I learned long ago, success breeds success. It is when we have just experienced success that we have the most confidence and the most enthusiasm. That excitement will come across in our voice and our actions, and make it much easier to sell someone new on our ideas, to get that appointment, or to get in the door.

When you hit failure or adversity, many people will advise you not to sit back and wallow in self-pity. My advice is that when you hit success, don't sit back and wallow in your own glory. You can celebrate, but don't wait too long to get back to work. Don't let the enthusiasm drain just when you get the momentum going.

THE GIVER'S HARVEST

"It is a universal law—we have to give before we get. We must plant the seeds before we reap the harvest. The more we sow, the more we reap. And in giving to others, we find ourselves blessed. The law works to give us back more than we have sown. The giver's harvest is always full."

—FROM *THE BEST OF SUCCESS*, COMPILED BY WYNN DAVIS

We do not live on this earth alone. Everything that we do affects the world around us. We cannot expect to take what we need all the time without giving something back. Often, what we don't realize is just how much we get back from giving to others.

Recently I watched a very moving news report of a ten-year-old boy who was dying of a rare thyroid cancer. You'd think that he would have enough to worry about without thinking of others. Not so. He asked his mother if he could spend his allowance money, which he had been saving up, to buy gifts for other children on the cancer ward. When the reporter asked little Charlie why he had done that, he told the reporter that it made him feel really good and forget about being sick himself.

Charlie can teach us all a lesson. Not only did he do a good deed for the other children, he made himself feel better by giving of himself. In the end, Charlie gave even more than he could have imagined. Through his illness, doctors were able to discover the gene mutation that caused his rare form of cancer. This may in turn make

146

it possible to test other children who come from at-risk families, and remove their thyroids before they become cancerous.

The fact that we include service to others as part of our lives is uniquely human. In their book *Animal Behavior: Readings from Scientific American,* Thomas Eisner and Edward O. Wilson write:

> *The more advanced an organism is in its general anatomical and physiological traits, the less well-integrated is the society to which it belongs. . . . A vertebrate society is little more than a loose confederation of families and individuals. Even when they exist as subordinate members of societies, vertebrates remain relatively selfish and aggressive. The single outstanding exception to this trend is man himself, who has retained the basic vertebrate traits, but has managed to balance them with coalitions, contracts, vastly improved communication, and long-range planning that includes premeditated acts of altruism.*

We all have the ability to serve others. This doesn't mean that we have to give up everything we have or want to do for the benefit of others. It means that whatever we choose to do, we should include others in our vision. Every high achiever I've ever known has talked about giving back to others. There are an infinite variety of ways you can give back to others. You can give money to charity, or volunteer your time, mentor someone who needs help—anything that comes from your heart to someone else's.

It is difficult to explain on paper the feeling you can get from helping others. Recently, I gave a speech to an organization called Project Core, which helps youths from thirteen to sixteen years old who have come from broken homes, whose parents are drug addicted, and who have committed minor offenses. It was the toughest audience I've ever presented to. At the end, when I had them smiling and feeling better about themselves, and even had a few of them ready to take action on their dreams, it was the highest feeling I could ever have. There's something wonderful about taking what you've learned over the years and sharing it with people who are less fortunate than you. As much as you help them, they give you back even more.

The ability to give service to others begins with how we serve ourselves. We must be good to ourselves, have faith in ourselves and what we're trying to do. Ken Blanchard, author of *The One-Minute Manager* and *Mission Possible,* says that one of the things that stops people from becoming true peak performers is their ego.

"I always define ego as 'Edging God Out,' " says Blanchard. "That means putting yourself in the center. People who are 'value-driven' are able to set worthy goals that help themselves as well as others. People who are 'ego-driven' are always trying to evaluate themselves by how other people see them.

"In my seminars I ask how many people have children. A lot of them raise their hands. I ask, 'How many of you love your children?' They all laugh and put their hands up. I say, 'How many of you love your children only if they're successful? If they're successful you love them, if they're not you don't.' Nobody puts a hand up. I say, 'You mean you love your kids unconditionally?' They all answer yes. I say, 'What would happen if you accepted that love for yourself? If you realized that God didn't make junk? And you knew that no matter what you did, you were still okay, you were still loved?' That permits you then to do things that are driven by your values, because your goodness is already taken care of."

THE CUSTOMER SERVICE MODEL

The most successful people, and the most successful companies, in the world are those that are value-driven. Of course, they want to make money. We need money to live. We all want to be able to support our families, to have certain material things, to be able to take a vacation now and again. We would like, if not to be vastly rich, then at least to live a comfortable life. There's nothing wrong with that.

But when I ask successful entrepreneurs how they became successful, not one of them answers me, "I set out to make a million and I did." Instead, all of them talk about delivering quality products to their customers. Their most important concern is customer service. It doesn't matter what type of business you have. Customer service applies to every business—and to our personal lives as well. We're always trying to "sell" something to someone else, whether it's a product or a point of view. So everything that's said about customer service in terms of sales applies to all parts of our lives.

Here's what several high achievers had to say about serving others:

Dave Thomas, founder and CEO of Wendy's: "Someone who was about to interview me once went into a Wendy's restaurant and said, 'I'm about to talk to Dave Thomas, so give me the best hamburger you can make.' The server replied, 'You're going to get the same hamburger we serve to every one of our customers.' That's customer service. We have an incredibly simple mission statement at Wendy's. Our objective is to try and please the customer. Customers want a restaurant that's clean. They want quality food. They want their order to be accurate, and they want you to be nice. If we take care of our customers one at a time, there's a good chance they will come back again. You don't have to be a brain surgeon to figure this out. Take care of your customers and they will come back again and again.

Geoffrey Brewer, executive editor, **Sales and Marketing Management** *magazine:* "We recently conducted a survey of purchasing managers. These are the customers, the people that salespeople are supposedly listening to. Seventy-eight percent of the purchasing managers said that salespeople offer less than average customer service. . . . Companies talk a lot about customer service, but I don't know if it's getting through.

"There was another interesting story that we did that showed how companies are benefiting from customer complaints. Instead of brushing off complaints, companies are saying, 'Okay, Ms. Complainer, tell me what the problem is.' They then put this information into a database and try to determine where they can improve customer service and customer relationships. They use these problems as opportunities for improvement."

Ron Popeil, entrepreneur, the "Einstein of Infomercials," inventor of the Vegematic, Popeil's Pocket Fisherman, the Popeil Pasta

Maker, etc., etc., etc.: "The product you bring forth to the customer had better be of good quality, or you're going to be in the dump. If you haven't delivered good quality, all the telemarketing and infomercials in the world are not going to do any good.

"We offer substantial customer service at our company. We're there to solve their problems, but we also see this as a great opportunity . . . for communicating with our customers. You end up being their friend. When people call you with a complaint, and you solve their problem, you can usually end up selling them something else because you have built their trust. They believe in you.

GIVING BACK TO OTHERS

"Your journey is not over once your goal is reached, your dream fulfilled, the truth attained. The journey is never over until you share what you have learned with others. Then and only then can you begin preparing yourself for your next adventure."
—ROBERT D. BALLARD, FROM *HOLD FAST YOUR DREAMS*

Sometimes when we look back over our lives, we see things that we might have done differently and realize the lessons we have learned. One person who has examined his life in this way is Radu Teodorescue, author of *Simply Fit* and personal trainer to such celebrities as Cindy Crawford, Matthew Broderick, and Regis Philbin. Radu came to this country many years ago and built up his now-famous exercise studio from scratch. He has seen much adversity along the way, but he says, "The result of your confrontation with adversity is really irrelevant in the long run because success lies in the fact that you dared to do it. Your success is going through adversity and being on the other side. Even if you fail, you learn so much, and you are so far ahead of where you were when you started. Failure makes us reflect more. I wish we would learn as much from success as we did from failure. Why don't we learn from our successes? Sometimes we take it for granted."

Radu's philosophy is that we have a responsibility to do more than just enjoy our success. "Imagine that the success has to be transmitted to another generation," he says. "I want to share my experience, my great ride, and give it to other people. I want to say, 'This is the way I got here. I don't want to say this is the way I got to failure, and don't do what I did.' "

One of the lessons Radu has learned along the way is to be part of a team, working with others to share expertise and experience.

Radu believes that one of the reasons he never achieved national success like Jack La Lanne is that he didn't really become a team player with other people in his industry. He feels he could have been more involved, and looked at what they did with a little bit more respect. He regrets that he "didn't make a contribution to society in the way I would have wished to. You have to team up with everybody in your field. They help you by the mistakes that they make. Some of them will show you how they achieved their success. Then you can contribute with your own experience and knowledge so that everyone can become even more successful."

"We have to understand that each one of us is a very important little piece of a watch," he says. "It doesn't matter how small the pieces are in the watch, each piece is crucial. Without that piece that watch will never show the right time—except twice a day.

"The success of a group is always much greater than the success of an individual. It's so important to be able to put your selfishness down and to sacrifice for the success of the group. That gives you such a feeling of total belonging. And that what you do is going to stay here, not just for one day or for one year. It's going to stay because the group is going to transmit it to another group for generations to come."

It is when we think of others that our true success begins. That doesn't mean we can't want things for ourselves. In fact, it's good to want things for ourselves. When I was interviewing radio personality "Cousin Brucie" Bruce Morrow for my own radio program, I asked what he saw as some of the traits of superstars in the music business. He gave me a surprising answer.

"What keeps them going generally is the big G word: Greed," he said. "There's nothing wrong with greed. There's nothing wrong with wanting to benefit from something that you love to do and that you work very hard at. So greed is all right as long as it is not the zenith point of your endeavor or your quest. I think it's very important to do something and be rewarded in life."

Cousin Brucie has had great rewards in life, although he didn't start out with good fortune. When he was twenty years old, he was a DJ at 1010 WINS radio in New York. There was an older man at the station who wanted Cousin Brucie's hours. Moneys were passed to the "right" people, and soon Cousin Brucie was out of a job. "Through that adversity I learned how to protect myself," says Morrow. "I learned how to fend for myself. I also learned that I never wanted to do to anyone else what was done to me. It helped me grow in a lot of ways."

Now that Cousin Brucie has experienced a great many rewards in life, he spends a good portion of his time giving back. He is founder of Variety the Children's Charity, which helps children with brain damage, heart disease, and craniofacial disorders. He calls this activity the "love of his life," and says that he finds he can always call on top achievers from all walks of life to help support the charity.

OUR IMPACT ON OTHERS

"A life is not important except for the impact it has on other lives."
—JACKIE ROBINSON

In the first chapter of this book, we met Ed Hearn, member of the 1986 World Champion New York Mets, who has lived a life overcoming one adversity after another. There were many, many times along the way when he could have given up—in fact, he almost did. Instead, he found a new life where he constantly gives back to others, and has a great impact on people everywhere he goes. He knows what this impact can mean to someone in the midst of great adversity, and takes the responsibility seriously. That's why he has strong opinions about some of today's athletes.

"Not too long ago someone asked Charles Barkley, the great basketball player, Is it your job to be a role model?" says Hearn. "And Barkley said, 'Absolutely not. Not my job. Families should be taking care of their kids. I'm not a role model.' He's right in one regard. Families should be taking care to raise their children. This country needs to get back to strong family values. But I've got news for Sir Charles. He's a role model whether he wants to be or not. He has no decision. The only decision he has is whether he wants to be a positive or negative role model. In today's society, professional athletes and entertainers are put up on a pedestal. Up on that pedestal, you don't have any option whether or not you want to be a role model.

"That's why Dennis Rodman's disappointed me so much. Here's a man who's had a tremendous basketball career, and squandered everything away, all the winnings he made as an athlete. He was just about dead broke. So what does he do? He comes out with a book that sits in every bookstore and every mall in this country. Here is this hero, this idol, this great basketball player, sitting on a motorcycle naked with a basketball covering his privates. What kind of message is that sending to our country?

"When I was a kid, my mother picked out books for me to read, maybe just a chapter a night. But the books she had me read were not Dennis Rodman–type books. They were books about athletes, people that I loved. Maybe they weren't about the biggest names in sports, but they always had positive material. They talked about the athletes' faith, their families. Paying the price for success. Goal setting. Persevering. All these ingredients that made them the true champions of life. Reading those stories laid the kind of foundation that allowed me to handle some of the challenges and grow as a person as I went through the world."

Ed Hearn lives by the saying "Become part of someone else's miracle, and it will come back to you." He started putting this into practice in 1987, when he was in the hospital waiting for X rays that would eventually reveal the shoulder injury that would end his baseball career. He should have been thinking about what he would do with his life if his career was now over. Instead, he kept thinking about some young children he had visited in a hospital just days before. And the more he thought about these children, the easier it was for him to deal with his own situation.

"There is no exercise better for the heart than reaching out and lifting people up," says Hearn. "Nothing will lift your spirit and sense of purpose more than doing things to help those around you. When you do things for other people, professionally or personally, neat things just seem to happen. . . . Selfishness gets us nowhere. When we serve others, the rewards are unlimited."

Ed Hearn is a perfect example of someone who has gone through great adversity only to come back stronger than ever. He is also a great example of the surprises that life can bring. This is how he puts it in his book *Conquering Life's Curves* (written with Gene Frenette):

When I celebrated winning the World Series with teammates, then took part in a ticker-tape parade and went to the White House to hear President Reagan acknowledge us, I thought that was the ultimate. Nothing I'd ever do would surpass that for excitement or fulfillment.

But you never know what you're really capable of until situations or circumstances force you to strive beyond what you ever thought possible.

Even if I played in the big leagues another ten years, maybe earned another World Series ring or two, I can honestly say I would not be impacting people's lives the way I do now.

I believe there's no greater satisfaction in life than knowing you've done something to help somebody else out. Whether that means going out and shoveling snow off someone's driveway or visiting them in the hospital, it doesn't matter. The size of the deed is irrelevant, but the satisfaction from serving someone in need is irreplaceable. . . .

I once thought there was nothing more important than becoming the next Johnny Bench. Life proved me wrong.

I once thought there was nothing sweeter than winning the World Series. Life proved me wrong.

I once thought all my medical problems and the adversities that accompanied them served no real purpose. Life proved me wrong. Years ago, I was on top of the baseball world with the '86 Mets. Who knows if I'll even be here in another ten years?

But I know this: I'm alive, and I'm going to keep swinging for the fences.

SEEK AND SERVE

Sometimes we're afraid to help others. We think we'll stick our noses in where we're not wanted. We're afraid of rejection. We're afraid it will take too much away from what we have. Often we simply feel we just don't know what we can do, or whom we should be helping.

The truth is that service is in the small things as well as in the large. You can serve everyone with whom you come in contact by taking an interest in who each person is and what he or she does. If it benefits you in the end, so much the better.

Not too long ago, I accompanied my wife to the doctor. While I was sitting in the waiting room, a pharmaceuticals salesman came in to talk to the doctor. He was told that the doctor was too busy, and he left without even getting a chance to make a sale. I've been in sales all my life and I work with a lot of companies helping them train their sales forces, and I know when a salesperson is in need of assistance. I ran out after this salesman, into the parking lot. I talked with him for fifteen minutes about where he'd come from, what kind of company he was working for. I asked him questions about his biggest challenges on the job. I gave him lots of suggestions about how he could meet those challenges and how to get through to the doctor. In the end, he not only thanked me for the advice, he gave me a lead to his company. He bought my audiotape program so he could get some more ideas from me. We both ended up benefiting from the situation.

Service, in its most general form, is when you sit down with people and try to understand what they're doing and how you can be of benefit to them, even if it's just being there to listen. This is just as important in your professional life as in your personal life. When you meet someone, seek out what's important to that person, what he or she does, what the person's goals are. Then think about how you can serve that person.

Whatever business you're in, your goal is to serve people to the best of your ability. If you're a gas station attendant, your goal is to give 110 percent to the customers, to give them more than they expect. If you're CEO of a large corporation, that's still your goal.

Life is not meant to be lived selfishly. The true key to living a successful life is to turn the focus from "how can I help myself" to "what can I do for others." Many years ago, William H. Danforth wrote a little book called *I Dare You*. In it he said, "Catch a passion for helping others and a richer life will come back to you." Whenever you find yourself off track, recognize that your center of focus is turned inward, toward yourself. As soon as you turn yourself around, everything will come back to you tenfold, as you focus on helping others. The more you impact other people's lives for the better, the greater your success becomes.

When you give service, you don't necessarily get an immediate reward. The reward may never come, or it may come at a much later, totally unexpected time. The more people you help in this life, the greater the chances that some of them will come back to help you. Some people you serve may never help you at all. You might not even get a thank-you. But it's that one person you thought you'd never hear from again who calls you out of the blue and says, "We need some help on a really exciting project, and I suddenly thought of you!"

It's easy to overlook the person who just might help you the most. The salesman at the doctor's office was so focused on getting in to the see the physician, he ignored (and annoyed) the receptionist. In many cases, the person out front has a lot more power than it would initially seem. He never thought to find out how he could make the receptionist's job (part of which was to shield the doctor from too many salespeople) easier. Had he made friends with her, she might have found a way to slip him into the doctor's schedule.

We have thousands of opportunities to be kind to others, to reach out to strangers. We've always got that ability within us, regardless of our environment or our position. And when we utilize it, the energy that is released is truly unbelievable.

There are those in life who say that you should give service without looking for rewards, that giving service is reward in itself. This may be true; we probably should give service to others out of the goodness of our hearts. And, as was said earlier, immediate rewards may not be forthcoming. But what's wrong with giving service knowing it will help you as well as somebody else? If my motive is to help you, and by helping you I help myself—where's the harm in that? If one party can benefit, why not two? It's the classic win-win situation.

The ultimate win-win situation in life is to know that you have tamed fear and used it to push you onward; to give everything you do 100 percent effort and to utilize the abilities you have been given; and to give back to others in whatever ways you can, large or small.

There is a wonderful definition of success by the poet Ralph Waldo Emerson that says it all:

> *To laugh often and much; to win the respect of intelligent people and the affection of children; to earn the appreciation of honest critics and endure the betrayal of false friends; to appreciate beauty, to find the best in others; to leave the world a bit better, whether by a healthy child, a garden patch, or a redeemed social condition; to know even one life has breathed easier because you have lived. This is to have succeeded.*

seven

The Diamond Collection: The 60 Essential Facets of FOCUS

Diamonds Under Pressure

1. Humans are like diamonds in many ways. Our character, the purest and toughest part of ourselves, is formed deep within us, and often rises to the surface only when the pressure is greatest.

2. Animals have developed coping mechanisms that have evolved over hundreds and hundreds of years. The difference between human beings and animals is that we don't have to wait hundreds of years or rely on instinct to find ways of coping with adversity. When adversity strikes, we can make the necessary changes according to the way we perceive and interpret our environment.

3. The only way to get to success is to understand failure. *Every* successful person has had to face his or her share of adversity, obsta-

cles, and outright defeat. *Every* successful person has had to struggle with deep-seated fears and self-doubt. And every successful person has learned how to put fear and failure into proper perspective, to gain strength and knowledge from difficulty. Successful individuals know that success only comes from repeated triumphs over adverse conditions, and that mistakes provide information for future attempts.

4. We are at our worst and most desperate when we feel that everything is out of our control; that there is nothing we can *do* to help ourselves. But there is something we can do. There is a powerful tool we can use to help regain the control we need. That tool is called FOCUS, and the components are **F**oresight and **F**aith; **O**rganization; **C**oncentrated Effort and **C**ourage; **U**nderstanding; and **S**eeding and **S**ervice.

5. It is feelings of helplessness that lead to feelings of hopelessness. Once you begin to make practical, tangible plans for your future, that future can become a reality.

6. You can let adversity pull you down, or you can use it as a life force to spur you on to great accomplishments. It's your interpretation, your perspective on your circumstances, that determines which road you take. You can control how you react to adversity. We all have a choice to make, and it has been proven over and over again that it is not what happens to us in life that counts, but what we choose to do about it.

7. Each and every one of us has great potential within. We are diamonds under pressure, and we can let that pressure destroy us, or

allow it to force the best of us to rise to the surface. It is up to each and every one of us to make that choice.

Foresight and Faith

8. We are the architects of our lives. It is the vision that we create, the picture we hold up before us, that determines where we end up. What we can imagine ourselves to be becomes the foundation for the metamorphosis of every dream we have from a wish into reality.

9. A vision, once developed, needs to be nurtured and supported to be sustained. There are tools you can use to strengthen your vision and keep it focused and clear, and there are ways you can use your vision to spur you on to take action. Here are some visionary tools:

- Make your vision real to you.
- Look to your past to shore up your future.
- Surround yourself with images of success.
- Visualize your own success.

10. Every time you use visualization as a tool, you set up the circuitry in your mind to attract success. Once this circuitry is in place, the incredible power of the human mind attracts a positive result. The subconscious keeps your vision intact even when you're not consciously aware of it. And, as long as the vision remains strong, the subconscious will keep directing you to take actions that will lead to making that vision a reality.

11. Faith and foresight are what ground us in life. They keep us

stable, and keep us from crumbling when the winds of adversity try and blow us down. If you build your life on a foundation of ethics and integrity, you can handle the rough spots with grace and courage. Your choices become easier because you know there are certain lines you will not cross.

12. Everyone has his or her own particular skills and talents, and his or her own dreams and goals. The dream itself doesn't matter, as long as it meets these criteria:

- It is beneficial to yourself and to those around you.
- It allows you to utilize your skills and talents.
- It is something you believe in so strongly that no adversity can keep you from pursuing it.

13. What do you do if you're not sure what your passion is? You can start by listing "positive desires": positive, constructive things you're interested in pursuing. Make a list of twelve positive desires. Share them with a friend or partner. Then eliminate six of them, and discuss the remaining six with your partner. Then eliminate three, keeping one long-range and two short-range desires. Have your partner do the same with his or her list, and support each other on these desires.

14. Follow the way of the warrior:

- A warrior assumes responsibility.
- A warrior humbles himself or herself to all creation.
- A warrior learns the power of giving.
- A warrior takes responsibility, humility, and the power of

giving, and centers them around his or her core of spirituality.

15. It is quiet observance and reverence for the world surrounding us that is true spirituality. How you choose to define your faith is a strictly personal decision. But most top achievers do believe in some power higher than themselves.

16. When we look around and see the miracles that surround us—art and literature, beauty and grace, technology and science, and life itself—how can we doubt that there is something greater than ourselves? Adversity cannot get the better of us when faith is there to hold us up and keep us strong.

Organization

17. When we set goals that are important to us, they act as a magnet to keep us moving forward in a positive direction. Dreams do not come true by luck or magic; they become a reality because we set small, achievable goals that are accomplished step by step, day by day.

18. The acronym for GOALS:

- **G**ather as much information as possible.
- **O**rganize a step-by-step plan.
- **A**ct on your plans.
- **L**ook back at the plan and reevaluate your goals.
- **S**et new goals.

19. One needs to plan things out so carefully, and take care of all the minor details, minutia, and small steps as they arise, so that in the end there is very little left to be done.

20. Having a clear purpose, setting strong goals, and applying strategic thinking can help you defeat even the strongest "enemy" or adversity.

21. A simple system to determine what goals are most important to you and to go about achieving those goals:

- Take a piece of paper and write down ten goals for the next twelve months.
- Choose the most important goal on the list. Ask yourself, "Which one of these goals, if I were to achieve it, would have the greatest impact on my life?" Write your goal out as a question, such as "How can I increase my income to fifty thousand dollars a year over the next twelve months?"
- Write down twenty answers to the question.
- Choose one of the twenty items on your list, and *do it now*.

22. Everything is achievable if you're willing to put in the effort, and to make certain compromises and sacrifices. You may have to give your dream more time than you initially planned, or make it happen on a smaller scale. You will hit a lot of obstacles; you will experience failure. But the failures you have will bring you closer to success.

23. In order to reach our goals, we must create reality-based ac-

tion: break down large goals into manageable daily actions, what we need to do every day, every week, every month.

24. Adapt this business plan for life to lay out your goals and the necessary steps to reach them:

Executive Summary
- General overview/description of plan or goal
- What is the overall strategy for achieving that goal?
- What makes you uniquely qualified to pursue this goal?

Background
- How did the idea come about?
- When did you start working on this idea?
- What has happened since its inception?

Product
- What is the product (or the desired end result)?
- How does the product, service, or idea work?
- What is the value proposition (what benefits does it offer users)?

Marketing
- Who is the customer/beneficiary of this product or service?
- What are people doing today in the absence of the product, service, or idea?
- How will the product, service, or idea be priced?
- How will it be promoted or distributed?

Competition
- Who or what is in competition with your product, service, or idea?
- If competition is not relevant, are you trying to raise your own standards? From what to what?

Organization
- When this goal is reached, can it be managed and maintained by you alone?
- If not, who can help you manage and maintain the goal?
- What experience do you (and your potential partners) have in managing your particular goal?

Financial
- How much capital is needed?
- What specifically will the money be used for?
- How much money has been invested in the project so far?
- Can you realistically project profits (financial and otherwise) of attaining this goal?

Following this plan will bring any goal into a reality-based action plan. It will also clarify your thinking, so that if it is necessary to explain your ideas to someone else, you will be able to present them logically and concisely.

25. Goals are not written in stone. Adjustments can always be made.

26. Success is attained by setting goals and following through. When you're afraid to set important goals because they appear distant

and unreachable, don't think of yourself as starting at Point A and magically arriving at Point B. Instead, envision yourself going through each step, learning from your mistakes, and, most of all, *enjoying yourself and your great adventure.*

Concentrated Effort and Courage

27. We mustn't be afraid of adversity, for instead of grinding us down, it can polish us up to brilliance. We mustn't be afraid of resistance; remember the kite always rises against the wind, not with it. And we mustn't be afraid of pressure, for it's that very pressure that forms the diamond, the toughest, most beautiful stone on earth.

28. Be sure you have a reason to remain persistent. Every step you take must be of value, to yourself and to other people. Ninety-nine percent of the time, reaching your goal means interaction with other people. Try to understand what their goals are, as well as your own. Learn what's important to them, and what you can bring to the table to help them. It's not just increasing the quantity of your actions that counts, it's making every action more efficient.

29. Persistence also means constant improvement. If you keep doing the same thing over and over again, in just the same way, you'll always get the same results. So as you keep going, you must learn from every step you take. When that happens as you continue your efforts, you'll find shortcuts that increase your efficiency and make each action more meaningful than the last.

30. Remember the essence of Kung Fu: Accomplishment through effort.

31. You don't have to become a master of Kung Fu to succeed. You can become a master of whatever you pursue by adding discipline and patience, by practicing your craft over and over, no matter how many times you fall or fail, and by believing that in the end you will be successful.

32. Once adversity strikes, it's too late to prepare yourself mentally. That's why many people fall apart. They don't expect to fail, and when they do, they have no psychological reserves. And when they quit, they set up a habit of quitting. The most successful people develop a habit of persistence. Successful people think about quitting, too—they just don't do it.

33. We are given only one life, and we are given each day only once. The saddest people on earth are those who live in regret for not taking advantage of the gifts and opportunities they were given. And most regret is not about actions that were taken but we wish hadn't been; most regret is about things we did not do.

34. The world would be a much poorer place if it wasn't for the persistence and hard work of artists like Matisse and Michelangelo. These artists did not settle for the easy paths in life. To them, each brush stroke, each pounding of the hammer and chisel, was the true challenge. In life, it is each little step that contains the seed of great art. Life is in the journey, not the destination. As we go through our daily challenges, we should realize that that is where the greatness lies. That is where the learning lies; that is where the excitement lies. When the destination is reached, it's time to move on to the next challenge.

35. When a pole-vaulter jumps high, they raise the bar another inch and say, "Try for more." It's important to keep the pole-vaulting analogy in mind during those times when we want to sit back and take it easy, simply because we may have made some small gains, or taken a step toward our goals. That is just the time to raise the bar again.

36. Courage does not mean the absence of fear. Those who are without fear are reckless and thoughtless, and often cause harm to themselves and others. Those who have courage know fear, yet carry on despite it. They are able to look fear in the face, acknowledge it, and say, "I will not let you stop me."

37. Every time we step up to try something we've never done before, we learn more than we ever expect. The uniqueness of the experience gives us insights we could never get except by taking an action. When we venture out into new worlds we open our minds and our senses to things we might never otherwise experience. Our knowledge of the world expands tremendously with each new step we take.

38. Courage and fear are inevitably intertwined. We become courageous when faith meets fear and we take action. When we believe strongly in what we're doing, and we're moving toward a goal that challenges all of our senses, we meet fear head-on.

Understanding

39. We all suffer adversities in our lives. We all feel pressure of varying degrees. We all make mistakes and have to live with the

consequences. But it is not the mistakes we make in life that hurt us. It is *not learning* from those mistakes that leads to failure. The greatest gift we can give ourselves is the search for understanding.

40. Understanding is a combination of comprehension and personal interpretation. We must discover the facts behind the things that affect us, and then figure out what they mean to us.

41. Experience and action must always be accompanied by understanding. When we're lost, when we're depressed, when we are discouraged and can't find a way out, it is understanding that leads us back to solid ground. There are three basic aspects of understanding that can help us alleviate pressure and overcome adversity. They are

- Understanding stress and pressure
- Becoming an "expert" in your field
- Learning from others

42. When daily demands become overwhelming, it is time to go back to FOCUS. When we become confused and anxious, it's because we've lost our focus. When we lose focus, we give up. When we experience the stress that obstacles and adversity present, and look for the lessons learned, we can return stress to its optimum level.

43. We can't eliminate stress from our lives. But we can cope with it, and keep it at manageable levels. Here are six ways to manage the pressure in your life:

- Take a step back.
- Clarify your values and relationships.

- Seek and establish a balance.
- Practice your communication skills.
- Analyze your environment.
- Take action.

44. In the context of adversity, the object of obtaining knowledge is to eliminate fear. The more we know about something, the less fearful it becomes. You'll find that successful people don't have any less fear than anyone else, they just have more knowledge. They know their business inside out. We attack fear—we overwhelm it— by becoming an expert in our field of endeavor.

45. The only competition you really face is yourself. Can you do better than you've done before? Can you beat your own record? When your focus is on what someone else is doing, you diminish your own chances at success. You will succeed when you change your focus from competing with others to creating from within yourself.

46. If you think you "haven't got time," review your goals, every day if necessary, and ask yourself, "What do I need to do today to get closer to my goal?"

47. If you think you're too old to try something, remember that scientists have shown that the brain is a "use it or lose it" muscle; if we continue to stimulate the muscle into our later years, the probability of developing Alzheimer's and other age-related disorders lessens considerably.

48. If you think you're too young, remember that sometimes the

innocence and enthusiasm of youth work in your favor. People are often willing to help out a newcomer—they remember their own shaky beginnings and want to help others just getting started.

49. If you think you have too many responsibilities to pursue your goals, remember that we spend a lot of time trying to sell ourselves out of taking action and convincing ourselves it's not the right time. Even if it's not the right time, it's still the best time.

50. If you think, I couldn't do that, instead of letting your initial reaction, which is based on fear, make the decision for you, why not say instead, "That's interesting. I wonder what would happen if I tried that."

51. Excuses keep us from taking action. The longer we put off taking action, the stronger the fear and the excuses become. There is no guarantee that you will succeed at everything you try; the only guarantee is the failure that comes with never having tried at all.

52. Everyone should have at least five mentors in his or her life, including family, friends, colleagues, and peers. Anyone whose judgment you respect can be a mentor, as long as that person does not possess the following qualities:

- Mentors should not be people who have a negative attitude, who try to put you down and pull you down because you're trying to do something unique or unusual.
- They should not be people who think you can do no wrong, and who might have difficulty giving you constructive advice.

- They should not be people who are anxious to tell you how they, or someone they know, failed at just the thing you are trying to do. If you want to know how to fail at something, find someone who failed and they'll teach you their "success." If you want to learn success, find someone who is successful and they'll share their knowledge and experience with you.

Seeding and Service

53. When you're attempting to get something accomplished, you may try a lot of things that don't work out. You may hit dead ends. You may call on a lot of people who can't help you. But maybe, by making all those calls, you'll come across that one person who can't help you directly, but who knows someone who can. Here are some suggestions to help make seeding work for you:

- Make sure you've got the garden covered.
- Don't give up before the miracle.
- Learn from seeds that don't germinate.
- Ask others to help you seed.
- Take pleasure in the process.

54. Making connections means knowing how to seed so that you set up win-win situations for yourself and all other parties. Try to help other people reach their goals while you're trying to reach your own.

55. After you experience any kind of success, it is very tempting to sit back on your heels and spend time congratulating yourself.

After all, you have just successfully accomplished a goal. The best thing you can do is begin immediately working toward another goal. Why? Because success breeds success.

56. When you hit success, don't sit back and wallow in your own glory. You can celebrate, but don't wait too long to get back to work. Don't let the enthusiasm drain just when you get the momentum going.

57. We do not live on this earth alone. Everything that we do affects the world around us. We cannot expect to take what we need all the time without giving something back. Often, what we don't realize is just how much we get back from giving to others.

58. The ability to give service to others begins with how we serve ourselves. We must be good to ourselves, and have faith in ourselves and what we're trying to do.

59. Service is in the small things as well as in the large. You can serve everyone with whom you come in contact by taking an interest in who each person is and what he or she does. If it benefits you in the end, so much the better.

60. The ultimate win-win situation in life is to know that you have tamed fear and used it to push you onward; to give everything you do 100 percent effort and to utilize the abilities you have been given; and to give back to others in whatever ways you can, large or small.

Epilogue

I HOPE THAT what you've understood from reading this book is that you, who have suffered setbacks, adversity, and failure, are not alone. Very few things are true all of the time in all situations, but this is a universal truth: Plans do not become achievements, dreams do not become realities, ideas do not come to fruition, without setbacks, adversity, and failure.

I wrote this book to encourage you to take chances, to take calculated risks, and to allow yourself to fail. Failure teaches us unparalleled lessons that sharpen our survival instincts and give us a chance to reassess and reevaluate our lives. As Michael Korda once said, "It is on the way down that we learn how things work. On the way up, we are enjoying the ride too much to pay attention.".

The stories of high achievers presented in this book are gifts to you from the people who opened their hearts and lives to me. Learn from, and lean on, these stories. Know that all the adversity that has befallen these people has made them stronger than they ever thought they could become. When it's your turn to jump out into the unknown and try something scary, just remember those people who have been out there before and lived to tell the tale.

I didn't write this book so that you would go out looking for failure. But I did want you to know that if—when—you go out into the world and shoot for something challenging, you can expect obstacles and barriers to shadow your every move. The most important part of this book, however, is the knowledge that no obstacle or barrier is permanent when you use FOCUS as a tool to overcome adversity. Adversity is no longer something to fear. In fact, the only way you'll know you're reaching a pinnacle of success is if those setbacks and failures are hitting you along the way.

Adversity is a testing of the will. But now, with the FOCUS acronym, you have a resource that's designed to help you get through those tough times. The powerful action plans brought to you through the FOCUS acronym can be applied to any adversity, large or small, as has been demonstrated by the interviews and comments you read in these chapters.

Once you understand adversity, setbacks, and rejection as opportunities to gain powerful personal and professional insights, as chances to find out who you really are and just what you're made of, then you will excel further than most people. You won't be afraid to take those jumps out into the unknown. You can stand on the shoulders of others who have experienced adversities far worse than your own, and know that it is possible to come through to the other side.

Epilogue

If this book has made just one of you feel better about your own situation, if it has given one of you the courage to go after your dreams notwithstanding the possibility of failure, if it has provided you with just a few practical tools to help you accomplish your goals, then I have done my job; and you, despite of and because of the pressure, have become a diamond.

Bibliography

Andreas, Steve and Charles Faulkner, eds. *NLP: The New Technology of Achievement*. New York: William Morrow & Company, Inc., 1994.

Attenborough, David. *The Trials of Life: A Natural History of Animal Behavior*. London: William Collins Sons & Co., Ltd., 1990.

Bennis, Warren and Robert Townsend. *Reinventing Leadership: Strategies to Empower the Organization*. New York: William Morrow & Company, Inc., 1995.

Chow, David and Richard Spangler. *Kung Fu: History, Philosophy and Technique*. Burbank, CA: Unique Publications, Inc., 1982.

Danforth, William H. *I Dare You!* St. Louis, MO: American Youth Foundation, 1991.

Davis, Wynn, ed. *The Best of Success: A Treasury of Success Ideas*. Lombard, IL: Great Quotations Publishing Co., 1988.

Farber, Barry J. *Diamond in the Rough*. New York: Berkley, 1995.

Green, Timothy. *The World of Diamonds*. New York: William Morrow & Company, Inc., 1981.

Korda, Michael. *Success!* New York: Random House, 1977.

Lamott, Anne. *Bird by Bird: Some Instructions on Writing and Life*. New York: Anchor Books, 1994.

BIBLIOGRAPHY

Legrand, Jacques. *Diamonds: Myth, Magic and Reality*. New York: Crown Publishers, 1980.

Sun, Tzu. *The Art of War*. Translated by Thomas Cleary. Boston, MA: Shambhala Publications, Inc., 1988.

BARRY J. FARBER

Motivation ◆ 10 DIAMOND FACETS FOR SUCCESS

Based on his bestselling book and audio program *Diamond in the Rough*, this program covers the essential qualities for success based on topics such as: keeping the FOCUS in times of adversity, building and maintaining a strong attitude, goal setting and time management, serving others, the value of persistence and tenacity, building a team of mentors, creating passion and enthusiasm, learning how we learn, keeping your sense of humor, and much more.

"Barry Farber's program is the best mental training you can get!"
—BRUCE JENNER, Olympic Gold Medalist

Sales ◆ SUPERSTAR SALES SECRETS

This program will leave your audience with powerful and useful ideas to impact your sales immediately. With over twenty years of success in sales, Barry will share with you proven techniques that work no matter what you're selling. Some of the topics he covers include: gaining access to new accounts, questioning and qualifying techniques, handling objections, selling value, networking, listening skills, building relationships, closing, follow-up and follow through, and twenty characteristics of a top sales producer.

"Barry Farber knows so much about sales and marketing that he has forgotten more than most people can remember."
—KEN BLANCHARD, Coauthor, *The One Minute Manager*

Leadership ◆ TRAITS OF GREAT LEADERS

This high impact program prepares managers with practical tools and skills that can be utilized immediately in the field. Some of the topics include: building a strong team, how to recruit and hire effectively, coaching and counseling skills, creating a motivating environment, achieving goals through people not for them, growing the business, time and activity management, and running successful meetings.

"What a resounding success! The seminar you conducted for our Management Team was outstanding!"
—JO C. JERMAN, Vice-President, Merck

Customer Service ◆ SECRETS FROM YOUR CUSTOMERS

This program goes beyond customer service. It is based on thousands of sales secrets from actual customers who are sold to by the top firms in their industry. What are the qualifications of the ideal vendor? How can companies improve their relationships with their customers and generate more business? Some other topics include: twenty-five sales secrets from the customer, ten reasons customers leave, six foundation blocks for a winning customer service strategy, and fifty ways to keep your customers.

"Barry's powerful and practical ideas come from his achievements in the real world of sales and business success. He's made a huge contribution to our national sales force!"
—JOE BOURDOW, President, Val-Pak

For more information about Barry J. Farber's books, tapes, radio shows, literary agency, seminars, or to schedule him for a presentation to your company or organization, contact:

Farber Training Systems, Inc.
The Diamond Group
66 East Sherbrooke Parkway
Livingston, NJ 07039
call (973) 535-9400
or fax (973) 535-9466

Also be sure to look for these books and bestselling audio programs:

Diamond in the Rough
(Berkley Books/Nightingale-Conant audio program)
State-of-the-Art Selling
(Career Press Books/Nightingale-Conant audio program)
Sales Secrets from Your Customers
(Career Press Books)
Superstar Sales Secrets
(Career Press Books)
Superstar Sales Manager's Secrets
(Career Press Books)